D0315843

KOREA

IN SEARCH OF THE COUNTRY, THE SOCIETY AND THE PEOPLE

UNMASKED

KOREA UNMASKED: IN SEARCH OF THE COUNTRY,
THE SOCIETY AND THE PEOPLE

Copyright 2002 by Won-bok Rhie.

All rights reserved. Except in the case of brief quotations, no part of this book may
be reproduced in any form without the written permission from the publisher,
Gimm-Young International, Inc.

The Korean edition of this book was published in 2002 by Gimm-Young Publishers, Inc.

For more information on Gimm-Young books, please contact Gimm-Young International,
Inc., 515-1 Pajubookcity, Munbal-ri, Gyoha-eup, Paju-si, Gyeonggi 413-756,
Republic of Korea

website: www.gimmyoung.com
e-mail: bestbook@gimmyoung.com
tel: 82-31-955-3104

Printed in Korea

First Edition: October 2002   New Edition: March 2005

ISBN: 978-89-349-1771-7 07910

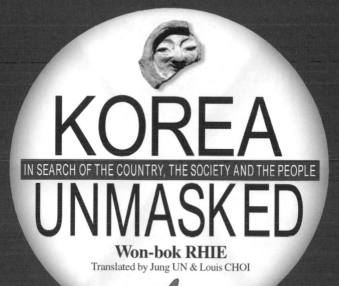

KOREA

IN SEARCH OF THE COUNTRY, THE SOCIETY AND THE PEOPLE

UNMASKED

Won-bok RHIE

Translated by Jung UN & Louis CHOI

gimm International
young

CONTENTS

FOREWORD

During the mid-19th century, geographer and cartographer Kim Jungho mapped the entire Korean peninsula for the first time in Korean history. If what Kim Jungho created at that time was the first "land map" of Korea, I would like this book to serve as an original "mind map" of the Korean consciousness. Unlike a "land map," however, that objectively delineates the earth's surface, the "mind map" in this book represents my own subjective views. I expect that there may be some who would disagree with my views, but I welcome any constructive discussions on the "mind map" of Korean society and its people portrayed in this book.

It has been some time since Korea, once known as the "hermit kingdom," emerged from obscurity and transformed itself into an economic powerhouse. Unfortunately, however, despite its status as the 11th largest trading nation in the world, Korea continues to be misunderstood by the outside world, which tends to pass judgment on the country solely based on the manifestations of the Korean attitude, but without taking into account the mindset that drives that very attitude. In fact, to a foreigner, Korea is an enigma, and it is often difficult, for example, to distinguish Korea from China or Japan. I believe this is partly attributable to the dearth of English language materials on Korea and its society and people. It is my hope that the English edition of this book will help such an audience better understand the inner workings of the Korean mindset and spark more interest in Korea. It is also my hope that this book will help young overseas Koreans in establishing their identities as people of Korean descent and in understanding what it means to "be Korean," especially in this day and age.

This is a meaningful book to me, as it is the latest addition to an existing 8-volume series of books on a number of European countries and Japan which I started working on more than 20 years ago. You may be curious as to why it took so long for me to work on *Korea Unmasked*, but, paradoxically, looking outwards before looking inwards gave me the perspective to objectively portray Korea in this book. It is, however, no surprise that *Korea Unmasked*, the latest to be published among the above series of books, is the first to be translated into English. This is so because, as I mentioned above, I believe there is a great need for a book like this that will help outsiders explore the inner workings of the Korean mindset and better understand Korean society and its people.

Korea is a fascinating and dynamic country worthy of a more in-depth look. You are invited to explore further and, through this book, I look forward to being your guide.

Won-bok Rhie
Seoul
September 2002

Introduction

* 'Hello' in Korean

* 2001 Korean National Office of Statistics

According to the World Bank, there are 229 countries in existence,

We have the most reliable statistics in town.

World Bank

among which legitimate data is available for 211.

Who knows the population of some of these countries?

Africa

So, it's probably safe to say there are around 200 countries.

200

The World Bank classifies these countries into three major groups.

Low-income	Per capita GNI US$ 755 or less
Mid-income	Per capita GNI US$756-$9,265
High-income	Per capita GNI US$9,266 or more

* GNI : Gross National Income

Count them, 50 high-income countries.

50

Those countries do pretty well for themselves.

growl

Korea reached the US$10,000 per capita GNI level in 1995, joining the illustrious group of high-income countries.

$10,000

Yeah, baby!

High-income

However, due to the impact of the Asian financial crisis in 1997, which caused the value of the U.S. Dollar to sharply appreciate against the Korean Won, Korea's per capita GNI dropped to US$8,490.

$8,490

Korea slipped to a mid-income nation.

South Korea sets record fall in unprecedented time!

crash

But, Korea has repaid the loans constituting the bailout package from the International Monetary Fund (IMF) early and it's back on track.

Debt free!

Outstanding! Super quick graduation!

IMF

Undoubtedly, Korea will rejoin the ranks of high-income countries in no time.

huff puff

In fact, Korea's doing pretty well for itself as the 11th largest trading nation in the world.

Thailand
The Philippines
Malaysia
Indonesia

Korea's Economy

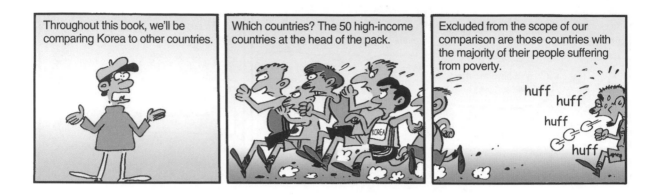

Throughout this book, we'll be comparing Korea to other countries.

Which countries? The 50 high-income countries at the head of the pack.

Excluded from the scope of our comparison are those countries with the majority of their people suffering from poverty.

huff huff huff huff

For instance, when we say "Korea recorded the fastest economic growth in the world,"

Korea

we're comparing Korea to the 50 high-income countries,

not the 200 some countries across the planet.

Country A
Country C
Country
Kuwait
Country
Burundi
Saudi Arabia

Why do we make this distinction? There are a lot of small countries out there.

During the 70s and 80s, Korea recorded an economic growth of 10% or more annually.

GNP 100 billion dollars
10 billion dollars
1974   1983

Some countries might have posted higher growth rates.

Our growth rate was much higher!

70 million dollars

5 million dollars

This point should be made clear from the outset in order to avoid any confusion.

This book's incorrect.

Korea Unmasked

Another reason for limiting the scope of our comparison is because we want to compare ourselves to those who are ahead of us and learn from them.

I... must... keep... up!

What's the point in comparing ourselves to countries that are way behind?

I've come far so shall I take a break?

KOR

Having made this point clear, let's begin!

We're only taking into account the 50 high-income nations in our comparisons!

Neighbors but Strangers:
Korea, China and Japan

As we discussed before, there are about 200 countries out there.

neighbor neighbor neighbor
neighbor
neighbor neighbor neighbor
neighbor
neighbor
me
neighbor neighbor

All of these countries co-exist with their neighboring countries.

Isolated island country here. Hello?

You still have neighbors, right?

Among all these countries, you won't find neighbors more different than Korea, China and Japan.

Ni hao!

Annyeongha seyo?

Konnichiwa!

中國 한국 ニホン

People say neighboring countries England, France and Germany are very different.

Good morning!

Bon jour!

Guten tag!

But look... Their people believe in the same God and Jesus Christ.

Jesus... The Virgin Mary!

England   France Germany

They all use the same letters, the alphabet.

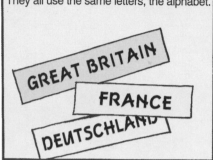

GREAT BRITAIN

FRANCE

DEUTSCHLAND

They all use forks and knives.

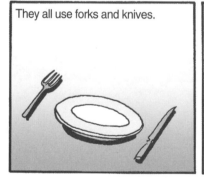

The three East Asian countries, on the other hand, don't even share these basic traits.

Let's look at these countries from the perspective of religion. China is said to be the land of Confucianism.

Confucius
552-479 B.C.

Among the hundreds of religions in China, however, Confucianism has become an underlying social and ethical philosophy, not a practicing religion.

How big a country is China?

In fact, more people have turned to Taoism, meditating for happier lives and tranquility.

Please let me earn a lot of money.

After communism overtook China, the Cultural Revolution greatly destroyed Confucian traditions.

waaa   Red Guard

Confucius is an enemy of the worker!

waaa

Turning to Japan, when Buddhism was first introduced,

practitioners of *Shinto*, the native religion of Japan, were anything but pleased.

Just say no to imported religion!

Prince Shotoku (574-622 A.D.) was the big man in Japan at the time.

Religious wars will end up killing us all.

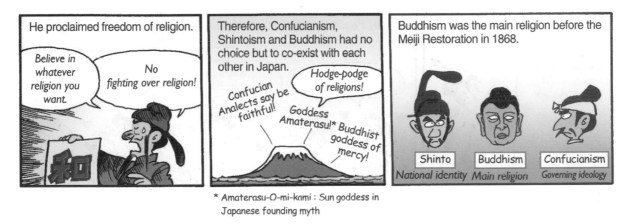

He proclaimed freedom of religion.

Believe in whatever religion you want.

No fighting over religion!

Therefore, Confucianism, Shintoism and Buddhism had no choice but to co-exist with each other in Japan.

Confucian Analects say be faithful!

Hodge-podge of religions!

Goddess Amaterasu!* Buddhist goddess of mercy!

* Amaterasu-O-mi-kami : Sun goddess in Japanese founding myth

Buddhism was the main religion before the Meiji Restoration in 1868.

Shinto	Buddhism	Confucianism
National identity	Main religion	Governing ideology

But in Korea, the Joseon* Dynasty (1392-1910) kings revered Confucianism, adopting it as the country's official religion, but they suppressed Buddhism.

Oppress Buddhism!

Revere Confucianism!

* Previously known as Choson

And Korea became the most Confucianism-centered country in the world.

Confucius says...

Mencius says...

Christianity spread after Korea's liberation from Japan in 1945.

Repent! Believe in the Lord and obtain salvation!

Amen!

Surpassing Buddhism, Christianity has become the No.1 religion in Korea with 35% of the population professing to be believers.

Others

It's a sight that cannot be seen anywhere else in Asia: tens of thousands of churches nationwide.

Those are all churches?

The religious manifestations in Korea are entirely different from those in Japan and China.

We're still a socialist country.

Buddhist goddess of mercy

Amen!

Religion's no big deal.

China

Korea

Japan

Although the Koreans, Chinese and Japanese all belong to the same Chinese-character-using cultural sphere,

中國
China

韓國
Korea

日本
Japan

東洋三國*

* 3 countries of the East

the Chinese use a simplified version of Chinese characters,

氣 → 气
從 → 从
車 → 车
歲 → 岁

the Japanese use two kinds of alphabets, *Hiragana* and *Katakana*

Katakana

バーゲンセール

Hiragana

お客さま
ありがとう
こざいました

テパート

and the Koreans use *Hangeul*, which was promulgated by King Sejong in 1446.

사은 대축제*
창고정리
대세일

* Bargain sale

Not only the written but also the spoken languages couldn't be more different.

Ling ling, Wo ai ni!*

Zheadema?**

Yeong-ja ssi, dangshineul saranghaeyo!*

Jeongmal?**

Eikosan, watashiwa kimi o aishiteru!*

Hontoni?**

* I love you.
** Really?

The English, French and Germans are supposed to be so different, but, at least, they all sleep on beds!

ZZZ

Likewise, the Chinese sleep on beds and sit in chairs.

囍

Meanwhile, the Japanese sleep on *tatami* mats,

while the Koreans sleep on a warm heated *ondol* floor covered with laminated paper.

Oh... oh... that hits the spot... This heated floor is so soothing!

The traditional clothing worn by people in these three countries are also unique.

Even the length of their chopsticks differ.

China | Korea | Japan

The Chinese eat a lot of deep-fried food.

sizzzle

They use long chopsticks as tools to pick up these foods.

Can't get oil on me. Must not get burned.

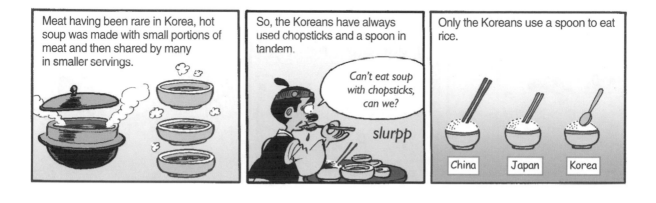

Meat having been rare in Korea, hot soup was made with small portions of meat and then shared by many in smaller servings.

So, the Koreans have always used chopsticks and a spoon in tandem.

Can't eat soup with chopsticks, can we?

slurpp

Only the Koreans use a spoon to eat rice.

China | Japan | Korea

Because chopsticks are only auxiliary utensils, the Koreans don't need long chopsticks like the Chinese.

In Japan, rice used to be precious and rare so people mixed various cereals when preparing meals.

kaoliang grain   *millet*

Adding cereals made the rice less glutinous. It was not easy for the Japanese to handle the slippery rice with chopsticks.

Crumble

Naturally, they brought the bowls close to their faces and shoveled in the rice.

Shorter chopsticks were more convenient.

These chopsticks are too long.

The Japanese still bring rice bowls close to their mouths. It's a hard habit to break.

My! He eats holding his rice bowl to his mouth!

Wow! He's eating with a spoon!

Although they are neighboring countries, Korea, Japan and China couldn't be more different.

It is hard to tell them apart just by their looks.

You're Chinese, right?

No, Korean!

Ways of thinking, value systems and lifestyles... We have nothing in common!

大中華 世界的中心

HUB KOREA !

脱亜入欧, 脱欧入亜？

What could be the reason?

Put simply, England, France and Germany have incessantly interacted and warred with each other.

Pow! Bam!

They've mixed and matched... throughout history.

England

Germany

France

They share common historical, cultural and social traits.

England

France

Germany

It's fair to say that the Koreans, Chinese and Japanese have also incessantly interacted with each other, but only to a certain degree.

To a greater degree, each country shut itself off from the others, forging its own unique history.

Don't...don't... No...no... Don't even look at those savages!

Just leave me alone!

Let's live amongst ourselves.

China

Korea

Japan

China considered itself as the center of the world.

中華

It paid little attention to Korea and Japan, which it considered to be remote, border countries.

Korean peninsula

Ever since the Mongol invasions, and up to the Ching Dynasty, various minority people have ruled China.

Since the T'ang Dynasty, the Chinese have embraced minorities with a policy of tolerance and cosmopolitanism.

Feisty little fellers. Come to daddy.

They put all the minority races into one big melting pot and stirred them into one culture centered on the Han culture.

Han culture

They brought all this together into one huge, unified culture.

We're all Chinese!

Time: 18th century... China was culturally far ahead of the West.

Wooo!

Ahhhh!

The Chinese weren't shaking in their boots because of foreign cultures. In fact, they let other cultures in without much concern.

You ask, "Shall we accept the cultures of savages?"

"Let them in!" I say. Our culture will soak them in like a sponge!

They believed that Chinese culture was the mainstream world culture. They were very proud and confident.

Culture of savages

Chinese culture

Let's turn the mike over to historian Arnold Toynbee.*

Mmm-hum... Yes... Yes... After the Han Dynasty... You see... The Chinese discarded their bellicosity and chose peace.

* Arnold Joseph Toynbee (1899~1975) : England

The concept of unity and peace forms the core of China's spirit, and cosmopolitanism the spirit of the Chinese.

Unity

Cosmopolitanism

Peace

However, because this 'unity and peace' was 'peace for unity,'

One China! One World!

Border country

Border

border countries like Korea were forced to submit to China.

We are one, I'm telling you!

Border countries that pursued independence faced non-stop Chinese invasions.

You claim independence? I don't think so.

And the main victim of all of this was Korea.

You won't listen to us and want to play alone again?

The Korean peninsula is just a tiny projection on the eastern side of the Chinese mainland.

Up until the early part of the Goryeo* Dynasty (918-1392 A.D.), the Koreans were able to fend off the Chinese.

Fierce!

But after the Mongol invasions, the unified China was too much for Korea.

* Previously known as Koryo

By the time of the Joseon period, Korea was forced to submit to the Chinese policies of 'unity' and 'peace.'

Goodness! I've heard enough already!

Korea agreed to become a vassal country of China on one condition:

All right! I'll call you big brother!

Independence of the Korean peninsula... even if a mere formality...

Keep your nose out of my business!

Let's suppose Korea didn't do this but openly and frequently interacted with the Chinese.

The two people would have mixed, and Korea would have lost its national identity.

Chinese

Koreans

Except for limited diplomatic and trading ties that were absolutely required,

If you're done with your business, go home!

Korea bolted its doors, and its people were prevented from mixing and mingling with foreigners.

Purpose of travel? Denied!

NO!

For 500 years, Korea was isolated... just like an island.

STOP   Korea

During those years, Korea developed its own unique culture and customs.

We're different!

What about Japan? They sit alone in the east.

At the end of the world...

After the failed Mongol invasions,

except in the case of the U.S. occupation after World War II,

You started the war! You pay for it!

Japan has lived without foreign invasions unlike most other Asian countries.

That's... *pretty impressive!*

Japan adapted both Korean and Chinese cultures... including Buddhism with open arms.

As an island country, it is necessary to open our doors to foreign cultures.

They absorbed foreign cultures with this unique islander mentality.

Foreign cultures

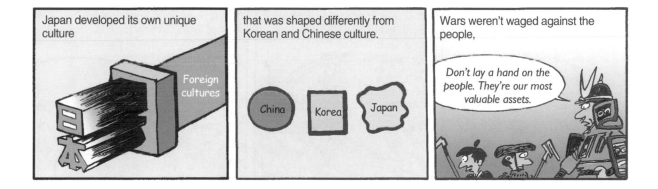

Japan developed its own unique culture

Foreign cultures

that was shaped differently from Korean and Chinese culture.

China   Korea   Japan

Wars weren't waged against the people,

Don't lay a hand on the people. They're our most valuable assets.

but between those in power, who were each struggling for the upper hand.

They're going at it again.

Attack! Hurrah!

Unlike the Chinese and Koreans, the Japanese lived without fear of a foreign invasion.

Instead of developing a large-scale, masculine culture, the Japanese developed a subtle, delicate and feminine culture.

These countries greatly differ from one another.

Yet, oddly enough, they share one common trait.

Regardless of the size of their population, they are each a homogeneous people.

The Chinese think of themselves as the center of the world. Chinese culture = world culture.

For thousands of years, the Chinese have preserved a unified country.

There are 1.3 billion people living in China today. They all consider themselves as Chinese.

The Koreans have suffered for thousands of years from recurring foreign invasions.

A national consciousness of unity developed as the Koreans came together to fend off foreign aggressors.

Having lived as one people since the Unified Shilla Dynasty (57 B.C. - 935 A.D.), a national spirit of camaraderie binds the Korean people.

The Japanese lived together for thousands of years, enduring many ups and downs.

The homogeneous Japanese population consists of 130 million people.

Because of this strong sense of homogeneity and camaraderie, compared to most western countries, it's easier to define the characters and cultures of Asian countries.

What is the most important value of each of the three East Asian countries?

一
ONE
FIRST
SOLO

China

忠
ORTHODOXY
ORIGINALITY

Korea

和
HARMONY
PEACE

Japan

What do the Koreans, Japanese and Chinese each consider to be the most important value?

An essential and irreplaceable value safeguarded by each people.

The most important value

In other words, what's the key to understanding their mind frames? Of course, there's no simple answer.

MIND FRAME

But if there is a one-word answer to this question for each country,

One word!

one would be the answer for the Chinese.

One

Why **one**? Let me try to explain.

You're trying to simplify us into this **one**?

One?

* 'Yi' in Chinese. 'Il' in Korean.

As you well know, China is a huge country.

100 times bigger than Korea!

In a country of such size, people with power were bound to sprout up all over the place.

They formed their own countries, and engaged in endless struggles with each other.

Each country attempted to expand its territory by waging war against its neighbors.

Never was there a day without a war.

clash

clash

The people were profoundly devastated, living in fear for their lives and suffering from poverty.

What was the lesson the Chinese learned after suffering through years and years of wars?

All we are saying is give peace a chance! No more wars!

Peace through might! This is only possible if somebody unifies the entire country through strength!

Only with an absolute, untouchable ruler and a strong, unified country could strife be avoided.

Absolute authority and a unified country

were required to achieve peace.

The Chinese realized this after suffering through many years of wars.

*Unified country = Peace
Division = War*

After Emperor Qin Shi Huangdi (259-210 B.C.) unified China in B.C.221,

B.C. 221

the Chinese struggled to remain as **one**, regardless of the price they had to pay.

Division

Except for certain periods of division, China remained unified for more than 2,000 years.

The Three Kingdoms

Nothern and Southern Dynasties

Unification Unification Unification

It's hard to find any other country in history that has managed to remain unified for that long.

Although it has been over 1,000 years since the fall of the Roman Empire, which lasted for a millennium,

...China's still unified!

We are the only one in the world.

But, no matter how strong the empire might've been,

China was just too enormous. How was it to govern every nook and cranny?

I'm a King!

Me, too!

Me, three!

Me, four!

China opened its arms, embracing all people living on the Chinese mainland with a cosmopolitan policy.

Stop all your fussing and come to daddy!

It adopted a policy of tolerance and compromise.

Scaring the daylights out of them on one side.

Patting and hugging them on the other.

Under the umbrella of this fundamental philosophy, they used a system of vassalage to keep China unified as **one** country.

My offering...

Under this system of vassalage,

We're not China's little brother.

You are if we say so!

as long as China was recognized as 'big brother,'

China promised autonomy... a status nothing short of independence.

I pledge my allegiance...

I grant you autonomy.

25

If one accepted its status as a part of China,

Big Bro!

China guaranteed self-governance and limited interference in domestic affairs.

Run naked through the woods. Wear your mama's clothes. We don't care.

In other words, China was at the top of a loose affiliation of border countries.

Centralized government

CHINA

Other | affiliated | countries

These border countries would send envoys to China every year packed with tributary gifts, pledging their devotion as loyal vassals.

But don't misunderstand – China wasn't extorting these 'gifts' from these countries.

Hey... hey! Give me this! Give me that!

I don't want to play with you anymore!

China

Because these gifts symbolized devotion, in order to appease these countries,

Please, no rebellions...

China would repay its vassals with gifts manyfold.

I'm so moved!

In Korea, during the Joseon period, the Koreans settled into brown-nosing the man in power.

Toadyism | Autonomy

The overpowering Chinese did interfere with domestic issues to a certain extent.

Change the prince!

This is the new queen? Uhh... I don't think so.

However, it could be said that Joseon maintained its independence for 500 years because of this vassalage system.

If we didn't submit, we would've been at war with China for 500 years.

Although the Koreans proudly claim that Korea was an independent country,

We were never a vassal country of China.

from the Chinese point of view, Korea was a part of China.

Listen! You paid the membership fees. You were a member of the China club!

After the Japanese defeated the Chinese in the Sino-Japanese War,*

Crouching tiger? More like paper tiger!

the first thing the Japanese did was to force China to recognize Joseon's independence from China.

You're an independent country, right?

Uhh... Umm... Yes that's right!

Why were the Japanese so adamant in separating Joseon from China? So that they could invade the Korean peninsula without worrying about China.

Yes... Yes... We are an independent country.

Good! Since this is a matter between two independent countries, stay out of it China!

* Sino-Japanese War : 1894-1895

What happened if a country refused to become a vassal country and proclaimed independence from China?

Separate country here!

The result would've been... endless brutal wars without boundaries or limits.

Crack!

This tradition of **oneness** has been China's fundamental policy that continues on to this day.

China is one! We're one no matter what!

China

The dissolution of the **one** China only meant strife, chaos and war.

ONE CHINA

The Chinese continue to embrace this belief and will never give up on it.

Immutable fundamental rule

One China

China has shown a great deal of tolerance regarding Taiwan.

They're a part of China...

It's only a matter of time before they come to papa...

Taiwan

China

But it would be a different story if... let's say... Taiwan claims, "We're not part of China. We're independent!"

Taiwan independence!

WHAT!

Taiwan

China

If Taiwan continues to assert its Independence,

Taiwan independence!

Impossible!

Taiwan

China has said that it wouldn't hesitate to go to war. This is the fundamental '**One China**' philosophy at work...

War will be your only friend if you continue!

Taiwan

In 1997, the United Kingdom returned Hong Kong to China after 99 years.

Hong Kong

True, the 'one country, two systems' policy is a product of the practical nature and policy of tolerance of China.

We're going to live the way we've always lived.

Sure!

Capitalism

Socialism

But remember... China allows this because Hong Kong has recognized itself as being a part of China... a Chinese territory.

Hong Kong is a Chinese territory!

Of course! Good boy! Now go and play!

Many Islamic people live in the region neighboring Central Asia.

Kazakhstan

Allah~~!

Kyrgyzstan

Tajikistan

Afghanistan

Pakistan

China

They desire independence from China and the formation of a separate Islamic state.

A separate Islamic state!

The Tibetans have also waged a fierce struggle to gain independence.

China forced us to merge in 1950.

We want independence!

Allowing these countries independence would mean their departure from the **oneness** of China.

Independent Country

One China

China would do whatever it takes, using all means necessary, to crush these movements for independence.

crush

*Having even one of these territories leave would mean an end to the civilized world as we know it! The breakdown of our supreme principle — the **oneness** of China. Never! It cannot be done! No! No!*

*The end of **one** China! This would lead to chaos and strife! The destruction of lives and property of the Chinese people!*

*A Unified China... Maintaining **One** China is the key to protecting the lives and property of the 1.3 billion people of China!*

This is why China makes such a big deal about being **One**.

The ethnic Koreans* living in China are allowed to speak and run broadcasts in their mother tongue.

But start digging your graves if you even utter the word independence.

* A large number of ethnic Koreans live in China.

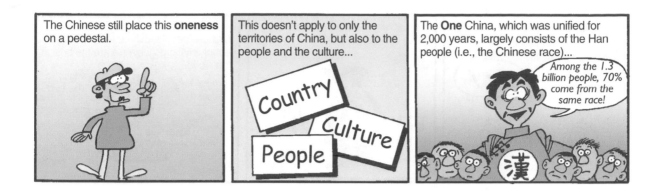

The Chinese still place this **oneness** on a pedestal.

This doesn't apply to only the territories of China, but also to the people and the culture...

Country
Culture
People

The **One** China, which was unified for 2,000 years, largely consists of the Han people (i.e., the Chinese race)...

Among the 1.3 billion people, 70% come from the same race!

漢

But China also absorbed the 50-some-odd minority people through its policy of inclusion and tolerance.

Minority people

Today, China has the largest population in the world. 1.3 billion!

Although I am ethnically Korean,

I am Chinese indeed.

Although there have been times when China was ruled by minority people,

the cultures of these minorities coalesced into the Han culture, thereby becoming part of the culture of **One** China.

Han culture

Minority people

Chinese

Meanwhile, 30 million Chinese emigrants live in various places around the world.

HOTEL
金山飯店
廣東文獻
香港通報
紅明藥
上海

Even these emigrants unite under the banner of **One** China.

"Wo shi Zhongguoren!"*
(我是中國人)

London Paris Rome LA New York

* I'm Chinese!

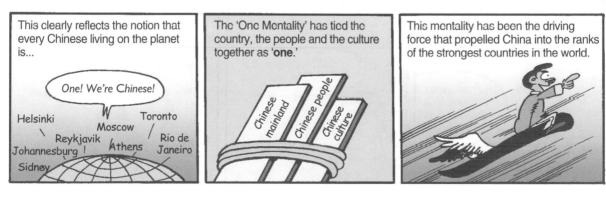

This clearly reflects the notion that every Chinese living on the planet is...

One! We're Chinese!

Helsinki
Moscow
Toronto
Reykjavik
Rio de Janeiro
Johannesburg
Athens
Sidney

The 'One Mentality' has tied the country, the people and the culture together as '**one**.'

Chinese mainland
Chinese people
Chinese culture

This mentality has been the driving force that propelled China into the ranks of the strongest countries in the world.

This Chinese character '一' means 'one' but it also means 'the best.'

Sinocentrism symbolizes the pride of the Chinese people.

In so many words, they think the Chinese people, culture and, in fact, just about anything Chinese are the best in the world.

Savages to the north

Savages to the east

Savages to the west

Barbarians to the south

This pride continued despite China having been disgraced by repeated invasions by world powers.

A savage has just broken my nose...

This pride is not just dreamy nostalgic reflections of China's glorious yesteryears...

Yesterday, all my troubles seemed so far away...

It's a confidence that permeates modern day China – a belief that they can be the greatest country, the superpower of the world.

2008 Beijing Olympic Games

Qualified for the 2002 World Cup.

7% economic growth!

Looking good! We're headed for the top!

Things were very different during the latter half of the 19th century. Western powers stepped on the ego of the Chinese. The world community disrespected them.

The Chinese are lazy and filthy!

What did Napoleon have to say after catching a glimpse of China's potential?

Monsieur, don't wake a sleeping lion!

But these European countries, which had only a fraction of China's population, rolled into China with their imperialistic policies and trampled over the country. China was insulted.

Distinguished and prominent European thinkers and philosophers, people we all know by name, mocked China.

A great country? Are we talking about the same country here?

Turn the mike over to Hegel*...

China is an enormous country that time forgot.

"Although China is an enormous country, nothing has changed for thousands of years. Only China's rulers, not its people, enjoy freedom."

2000 yrs ago   1000 yrs ago   Present

* Hegel : German philosopher

Step up to the mike, Karl Marx*...

China's stagnant... For thousands of years,

its leaders have been replaced but the lower class has never changed.

*K. Marx : German thinker

What did Friedrich Engels* have to say?

They're a very lazy people...

They don't have the will power to last in Asia!

*F. Engels : English thinker

Tell us your thoughts, Max Weber.*

The Chinese are passive and dull.

They lack sympathy and honor!

So tell us what you really think

*M. Weber : German philosopher

The self-indulgent observations of these Western thinkers show that they failed to see the potential power of the oneness of China.

We're so much better.

Armed with modern weapons, the invading imperialistic powers from the West pulverized the Chinese. Falling like dominos, the Chinese did look pitiful.

This is too easy

Bang

After the dissolution of the Soviet Union...

Russia's financial situation turned sour... despite its status as the largest country in the world.

Russia's economy

In contrast, look at the Chinese. They endured domestic strife between the Communists and the Nationalists... They went through the Cultural Revolution and much more.

Civil war

Cultural Revolution

Now, they have emerged as one of the strongest economic powers in the world.

Isn't this a product of their desire to become the 'best'?

CHINA

The Americans are moving quickly to arm themselves with a missile defense system (MD).

Missile Defense

Why? They've realized China will be the only superpower that will be able to go against America.

America's main enemy is now China!

Another meaning for the Chinese character '一' is 'solo.'

ONLY ME!

SOLO, ALONE

This also means that the Chinese tend to look out only for themselves.

The Chinese have suffered much throughout their history,

* 'Yi' in Chinese, 'il' in Korean

which led the Chinese to only trust themselves and their families.

They could care less about what happened to others.

They became self-centered, looking out only for themselves and their own good.

Devotion? That's hogwash!

Who is the king? It makes no difference to the people! I need to take care of myself.

As mentioned earlier, 1.3 billion people in China and tens of millions of people abroad unite under the banner of '**One** China.'

We're Chinese!

China is one!

We're the center of the world!

CHINA

But... and this is a big but... they're a very selfish people at the same time, looking out for only their own well-being and prosperity.

Me!

My kids, my wife!

Me!

My family!

This 'me only' mentality pervades the lives of the Chinese.

China has had a difficult history!

I may have been born in troubled waters but I'm going to die in comfort...

One China... the best culture... the 'me only' mentality...

Thus, the Chinese character '一' represents the values and mentality of the Chinese people.

That's the reason why China's most important value is represented by '一.' Interesting isn't it?

What would be the most important value of the Japanese then?

That's easy. That would be 'wa'.*

* 'Hwa' in Korean

What does *wa* mean? It means peace and harmony.

Peace and Harmony!

There are many words that contain 'wa'.

和親	和議
1. Friendship	5. Peace negotiation
和解	和好
2. Reconciliation	6. Harmonious
和氣	和樂
3. Geniality	7. Peaceful
和同	
4. Unison	

In other words, what all this boils down to is... 'let's live in harmony.'

I ask for your good will...

No... No... I ask for your good will...

How did peace and harmony, *wa*, become the most important national values to the Japanese?

Japan is an island country.

Tell me something I don't know!

Island countries are characterized by different traits than those of continental and peninsular countries.

Continent

Peninsula

Island

3 sides face the ocean

4 sides face the ocean

Different ethnic people were constantly at war in continental and peninsular countries...

waaa

wooo

For island countries, the ocean served as a natural barrier against foreign invasions.

Catch me if you can!

Na-na-na-nana!

The greatest danger for island countries didn't come from external threats but from internal struggles.

If an internal war erupted, the people living on the island had nowhere to run.

Row 1, Panel 1: To avoid such a tragedy, the people placed a so-called divine ruler at the top who, in actuality, had no real power...

All hail thee!

Row 1, Panel 2: Instead, another person with real power governed the people.

Row 1, Panel 3: So two systems coexisted.

Symbolic leader — Real leader

Head of state — Leader holding real power

Row 2, Panel 1: During the formative period of a country, one leader performs both functions.

Symbolic power

Real power

Row 2, Panel 2: Because of the special circumstances of island countries, after a long struggle, the structure of power shifts to the dual system.

Reigns — Rules

Symbol of country — Real power

Row 2, Panel 3: In Japan's case, during the early stages of the country, the *tenno* (emperor) reigned and ruled over the country.

Tenno

Imperial Court

Row 3, Panel 1: Eventually, the *tenno* was reduced to a mere figurehead.

Tenno

National symbol

Row 3, Panel 2: The *Bakufu* regime ruled the country instead.

Tenno

Shogun

Imperial Court — Bakufu

Puppet government — Real government

Row 3, Panel 3: The *Shogun* was, in essence, the emperor, and, for that matter, the real person in charge.

Execute him!

Row 4, Panel 1: Fellow island country England was like Japan in the beginning. The king was not a mere figurehead.

Row 4, Panel 2: But the king was eventually stripped of most of his powers.

Symbol of country — Real power

Row 4, Panel 3: Most of such powers are now vested in the prime minister and a parliament.

King

Symbol of country

Prime Minister

Parliament

Control of real power

England's Parliament and Japan's *Bakufu* essentially served the same roles.

Real power!

Bakufu   Parliament

The *Bakufu* regime was made up of the *bushi** class, which practically ruled Japan.

* Warrior

In England, the local feudal lords that gathered at Parliament constituted the ruling class.

Gentlemen!   Yes, sir!

This dual system characterizes the structure of power in island countries.

Among the G7 countries... only our two countries have kings.

In order to preserve '*wa*', i.e., in order for islanders to live in peace,

it was important for them to avoid conflict.

Avoid conflict...   Make the maximum effort to avoid confrontation.

Without the meeting of the hands, of course, no sound would be produced.

clap

If the hands don't meet... whiff... nothing... zero sound... peace...

It's a surefire way of avoiding confrontations and conflict.

Point of conflict

As basic as it sounds... there is no better way to maintain peace than to avoid bumping into each other.

Points of conflict

Avoiding conflict in order to preserve *wa*.

This way of thinking is deeply embedded in the psyche and customs of the Japanese.

It's the key to understanding the mentality of the Japanese!

— After you...

How is it possible to avoid running into each other?

Well, each person would have to foresee possible points of conflict and take measures to avoid such conflict.

careful

caution

Each person would have to understand what makes the other person tick.

He must be thirsty...

Thoughtful consideration of others, known as *kikubari* in Japanese,

I have an extra can of coke here.

I can't drink both. Would you help me finish it off?

is basic good manners to all Japanese.

If I forced the coke on him, I would've hurt his feelings.

Being considerate of the feelings of others means being amiable and gentle.

I'm all right...

But if it'll help you out, it would be my pleasure.

The Japanese demeanor is grounded in this amiable and gentle disposition... *yasashii*.

Next is the 7th floor.

I know. It's not like I can't count.

The world-renowned cordiality of the Japanese starts here.

Welcome!

The Japanese language follows this temperament—it's smooth and gentle.

I graciously thank you for your continuing concern.

Please, don't mention it. I'm the one who should feel gracious.

The use of rough language, especially curse words, is considered atrocious behavior.

Why I ought to... I ought to...

You could say Japan is Old World when it comes to curse words.

Are you an idiot?!

My God! How can he use such harsh language!

Very, very different from the Koreans...

Yo! You bastard, long time no see!

Goodness! To call a friend a...!

But the Japanese simply do not encroach upon the territory of another person.

And they don't do anything others might consider burdensome.

> Why not stay for dinner while you're here?

> Uhh... Umm... I really need to get home!

They seem to all live in their own little capsules.

With each person living in his or her own secure world, it would seem hard for them to get ____ together.

> You're you!

> I'm me!

But, when there's a common goal,

common goal

no other people unites better than the Japanese!

> Let's raise our department record!

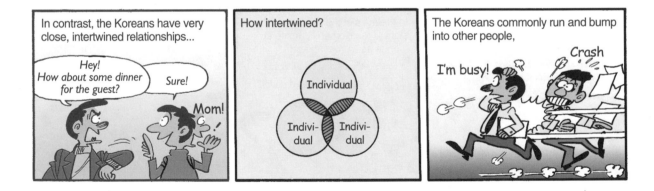

In contrast, the Koreans have very close, intertwined relationships...

> Hey! How about some dinner for the guest?

> Sure!

> Mom!

How intertwined?

The Koreans commonly run and bump into other people,

> I'm busy!

Crash

and the closer they get to people, the more they encroach upon their territories.

The Koreans also consider it perfectly natural for other people to encroach upon their territories.

Obviously, the Koreans and the Japanese have very different mentalities.

> The Japanese have no emotions!

> The Koreans are ill mannered.

In sum, the Japanese tend to avoid close direct contact with others while the Koreans tend to promote such contact.

The Japanese

The Koreans

The differences between these two countries are exemplified by the ways they approach videogames.

PS-II   PC

Videogame

Japanese kids tend to play video games alone.

zap zing zap zing

Sony Playstation... Sega...

Japan is the most advanced country in the world when it comes to creating games that can be played alone.

zap zap zap zap

It falls way behind, however, when it comes to games played with other people such as online games...

Online games? Too much contact with people...

NIPPON

Compared to Japan that has only a relatively small number of online games,

That's very weak for a country that supposedly leads the world in game development...

Japan

Korea offers dozens of online games.

Koreans get fired up by the competition.

Korea

The tens of thousands of Internet cafes spread across Korea are filled with young persons battling faceless enemies.

I'm going to beat you!

That's why these Internet cafes are exploding!

So, Japan is the most advanced country when it comes to offline games played alone,

zap zap zap

whereas Korea is the most advanced country when it comes to online games played with other people.

boing boing boing   zap zap

Just by looking at this, don't you get some idea of how different these two countries are?

I can't live alone. I get very bored.

I can't live with many people. Too uncomfortable...

The most important lesson Japanese parents teach their children:

Don't inconvenience others!

I don't want you to be a nuisance to others!

The Japanese avoid conflict with each other as much as possible.

Excuse me.

No. Excuse me.

They avoid possible points of conflict by being considerate of the feelings of others and by being nice and friendly.

You've been so gracious, I hardly know what to say.

Although it's not much, I offer a token of my appreciation.

The Japanese realize that it would be the end for all if they started fighting and quarreling in their confined island country.

I must be humble...

The more I'm humble, the fewer problems there will be...

They place *wa*, peace and harmony, ahead of other values.

和！

It's an absolute priority.

Avoid conflict at all costs!

和

Thus, you can understand why the Japanese act and think the way they do by understanding the concept of *wa*.

But it's hard for us to be genuinely sympathetic with each other...

Everything else is then crystal clear.

Wa → Elimination of points of conflict

→ Being considerate of others

→ Manners, kindness, gentleness

As discussed earlier, the Chinese consider...

'One' to be the most important value...

For the Japanese, it's *wa*.

和

What about the Koreans? Good question!

The answer can be traced to Korea's geographical location, the fact that it's a peninsula!

A peninsula is an extension of a continent, surrounded on three sides by water. Right?

Penin sula

A peninsula is 1/2 an island.

A peninsula serves as a natural bridge for continental countries to cross over and sail to islands.

Continent

Peninsula   Island

It's a two-way street — Island countries also use the peninsula to cross over into the continent.

Continent

Now, everything was just peachy for the Italian peninsula while the Romans were in power.

Italian peninsula

Nobody dared mess with the Romans.

You little...

But after the fall of the Roman Empire, all the European superpowers eyed the peninsula...

Grabbing Rome means being legit!

Rome

Before its unification in 1860, Italy was plagued by war for nearly 1,500 years!

France   Austria   Germany

Peninsular countries are strategically important.

Island

Continent

Peninsula

This was especially true in the case of Korea.

Continental powerhouse China was in one corner,

Those Koreans refuse to listen! War!

while ambitious Japan looking for the continental title was in the other corner.

Open a path to China or else!

In addition to these two powerhouses, numerous other foreigners incessantly committed aggressions upon Korea.

China

Japan

Border

countries

Japanese Pirates

43

The constant invasions and plundering greatly distressed the Koreans.

Their first priority was...

For survival, the Koreans had to be ready at all times to fight off foreign aggressors.

The Korean way of life was very wearisome.

Frequent foreign invasions result in frequent contact with foreigners,

which significantly increases the probability that different races would mix.

Suppose a particular race mixes with foreigners over a span of thousands of years.

What would happen? The bloodline, its racial identity, would eventually be lost.

For the sake of preserving their lineage... the Koreans became very exclusionary, discouraging the mixing with other races.

Look at the countries of the Balkan peninsula. They've suffered for nearly 2,000 years from foreign invaders.

But the people of each country did not mix with others, thereby enabling each such people to eventually survive as an independent race.

❶ Slovenia/Croatia/ Bosnia-Herzegovina/ New Yugoslavia
❷ Macedonia
❸ Rumania
❹ Bulgaria
❺ Albania
❻ Greece

This exclusionism is attributable to the survival instincts of peninsular people, i.e., their desire to preserve their racial lineage.

People of peninsular countries lived under the constant siege of foreign invaders,

struggling on a daily basis to survive, doing whatever it takes.

Fight or die!!

Inevitably, their personalities became very extreme.

Why so tough??

I need to survive!

With knives constantly at their throats, they had no time for diplomacy or compromise.

Let's resolve this through dialogue.

Only by winning can we live. What dialogue?

Win! Win! Win!

There was no choice but to be stubborn.

I'm always right! We have no other choice here!

Thus, people of peninsular countries tend to be stubborn.

Why are you so stubborn?

Because compromise means death!

Naturally, peninsular people came to possess different personalities compared to those folks living on the continental mainland and islands.

The Chinese — They emphasized unity to ensure peace and security.

Big land does not move far.

No worries!

The Japanese — They emphasized *wa* and avoided conflict to ensure peace and harmony.

What about the Koreans, who were victims of constant foreign invasions?

Advance *Attack!* *Hurrah*

The Koreans emphasized as their top priority the protection of their lives and possessions.

My stuff

The method by which the Koreans pursued this may be succinctly expressed by one Chinese character, read as '*choong*' in Korean.

忠 *

* *Choong*

45

The Koreans use the word *choong* as a prefix or suffix to other Chinese characters to make up words such as faithfulness and loyalty.

But the '*choong*' for the purposes of our discussion has an entirely different meaning.

No!

No!

忠

Let's go back to the original meaning of *choong* quoted in the lectures of Confucius.

孔子 *

* Confucius.

In his writings, Confucius says:

知忠必知中
Ji Choong Pil Ji Jung

In short, it means:

To know choong one must know the middle...

But what did he mean by the 'middle*'?

中

* Pronounced as 'joong' in Korean.

The Chinese character for 'middle' was modeled after the shape of a flag.

中

In the old days, the Chinese hoisted a flag in the middle of the village.

So, this character, '*joong*,' means middle or center.

Center

The true meaning of *joong* is 'the great essence of all things,' Confucius said.

中者天下之大本
*Joongja Cheonha Ji Daebon.**

* *Joong* is the great essence of all things.

In other words, the spirit of fairness and righteousness that is unfettered by private interests.

×

O

This is the mind of *daegongmusa*, i.e., fair, upright and honest disposition.

大公無私 *

Fair, upright and honest disposition

* Daegongmusa : Grand rulers do not seek private interests.

what does it really mean to be righteous, and fair to all people?

?

?

'Righteous to all people,' of course, doesn't mean 'what is right for only myself.'

Hey! As long as I do well!

No! I don't think so!

It is what all people or society considers as being upright.

Be good to your parents!

That's right!

YES

This applies to nearly everything-the Korean mentality, attitude and way of life...

This is right!

Rejecting or attempting to change this is absolutely unacceptable.

Put another way... you don't want to challenge what society deems to be correct.

Never to be changed

STOP

This leads to rigid conformance to the values that society believes to be the right values.

In other words, it is a 'yes' or 'no' dichotomy.

This is how the logic of 'seeing things in black and white' got started.

Yes

No

For example – 'commies are bad' is a common sentiment shared by the Koreans living on the divided Korean peninsula.

We can't let those commies in!

Korean society...

Why is communism bad? Isn't spreading everything equally an ideal philosophy?

won't accept people praising and accepting communism.

Commie Sympathizer! Red! Stone him!

As another example, all Korean people recognize that a harmonious family is a good thing.

Of course, harmony in the family is important...

Paradoxically, this is a trait that strikingly resembles socialism.

In a capitalist society, where individual wealth is not equally distributed,

such a trait is bound to disrupt the stability of society.

What kind of behavior does this equal profit mentality spark?

People work like crazy to acquire what others have.

I'm not falling behind!

This did wonders to promote the development of the Korean economy, as you can guess.

Economic growth rate

I did it!

Another important value emphasized by the Koreans is the preservation of the Korean identity.

Korean Identity

The Korean peninsula belongs to one people!

Having survived numerous foreign invasions, the Koreans didn't mix with other races.

I may lose everything but not this!

Pure Bloodline

The preservation of orthodox traditions was a legacy of the *choong* spirit.

Orthodoxy = Foundation of a nation

Legiti-macy

The emphasis on orthodoxy is not only limited to bloodline.

Tradition

Orthodoxy is the emphasis of 'original form.'

Original

원형(原形)*

The original form!

The original form is what the Koreans recognize as being legitimate and righteous.

Original

This is the original form!

Legitimate!

* Original form

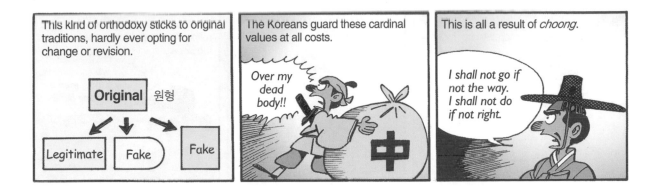

This kind of orthodoxy sticks to original traditions, hardly ever opting for change or revision.

The Koreans guard these cardinal values at all costs.

This is all a result of *choong*.

Okay then! As we've seen, the Korean character is well described by this one character, *choong*.

Choong stubbornly preserves values collectively recognized by the community.

Choong frowns upon fickle people that switch sides very quickly.

Choong believes in equal profit sharing.

Choong is exemplified by the extreme, sometimes radical temperament that developed over time

because of the constant foreign invasions.

Choong gave rise to the orthodoxy that rejects changes and distortions in an effort to preserve fundamental beliefs.

Choong... is the essence of the Korean character.

In fact, the many traits represented by *choong* are common traits peculiar to people of peninsular countries.

But the clearest manifestation of *choong* has to be the *seonbi* (scholar) spirit of the Koreans.

Seonbi

The *bushi*, Japan's ruling class, lived by a code of ethics known as the *Bushido*.

Bushi

On the other hand, the Korean ruling class armed themselves with the *seonbi* spirit.

We will not commit unjust acts, even if it means losing our lives!

Over time, the *seonbi* spirit formed the spiritual basis of the Korean nation.

Loyalty to country
Devotion to parents
Fraternity
Loyalty to friends

Today, this healthy spirit continues to flow in the soul of the Korean people.

Personal glory is second to Korea's prosperity!

This self-purifying (*jajeong*) spirit acts as a filter to the negative aspects of society...

Seonbi spirit

We're already aware that the *bushi* used to be the ruling class in Japan, right?

Ever since a *bushi* regime known as the Kamakura Bakufu came into power in 1192,

Nobility | Kamakura Bakufu

鎌倉幕府

the *bushi* class ruled Japan for nearly 700 years until the Meiji Restoration occurred in 1868.

Shogun

Leader of the bushi regime

The ruling class needed its own code of ethics.

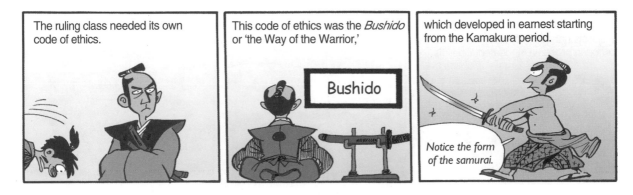

This code of ethics was the *Bushido* or 'the Way of the Warrior,'

Bushido

which developed in earnest starting from the Kamakura period.

Notice the form of the samurai.

The term *Bushido* started to be used during the Edo period (1603-1867).

Archer's code	Head archer's code
Soldier's code	Warrior's code

Bushido refers to the special code of ethics of the *bushi* warrior.

Respect honor and fear disgrace.

Such... Such disgrace... The only thing to do...

Train the mind and body for warfare... and build endurance.

husssh

Be faithful to one's master,

Commit suicide!

Yes!

and loyal to one's friend.

Thank you my friend...

Anything for a friend!

Typically, a *bushi* was not afraid to die for honor.

I fight for the honor of the Daira family!

Bushido not only formed the core of the soldier's mind but the spirit of the ruling class during the *Bakufu* period that was controlled by soldiers.

Bushido

On the contrary, the ruling class of Joseon picked up the pen, living by the *seonbi* code.

Seonbi

What is meant by *seonbi*? Although it occasionally referred to academics who did not hold any government posts...

Confucius says... Mencius says...

generally, people possessing both virtue and knowledge were referred to as *seonbis*.

Seonbinim!

ahem

A man of character, knowledge and virtue...

Seonbi = Man of character

The ruling class of Joseon society had to have this *seonbi* spirit.

That's why the people respect you.

The *seonbi* was expected to be loyal to the country.

A subject can't serve two kings!

King = The state

And kindhearted to the people...

The will of the people is the will of the heavens. I beg you not to turn a blind eye to the people.

He devoted his life to the pursuit of learning.

Etiquette and virtue you say? Just as important as one's life...

The *seonbi* mindset was characterized by impartiality.

I must not harm society just for the sake of my advancement.

The *seonbi* was not to covet unjust enrichment but to be a man of integrity and honesty.

You're trying to bribe me! Take it back!

The *seonbi* was expected to sacrifice his life in order to prevent the occurrence of what he considered to be unjust.

Although I've been sentenced to drink this bowl of poison,

I will not compromise my beliefs!

This *seonbi* spirit prompted the *seonbi* to express his views even with a sword to his throat.

It is unacceptable to delay the reforms!

When the king got off track, the *seonbi* would try to set things straight.

Realize that you have made a grave mistake!

When a national crisis emerged, the *seonbi* took the lead, spearheading the fight against invaders.

The fate of our country... is... like... a candle in the wind... Fight for your fatherland!

The Korean *seonbi* spirit and the Japanese *bushido* were both duties imposed on the ruling class, the equivalent to the concept of *noblesse oblige* in the West.

Noblesse oblige

Fair to say the *choong* mentality was at the heart of the *seonbi* spirit.

Seonbi spirit

Here's a list of virtues which members of Korean society were to abide by:

Choong

Filial piety

Benevol-ence

Faithful ness

Righteous ness

The preservation of archetypes also led to the strict adherence to these virtues.

Need to be practical instead of sticking to archetypes!

It may be impractical at times but preserving our roots and our origins is more important!

Me practical

Me original

Thus, a person, regardless of the degree of his success, was branded as an immoral person if he lacked these key virtues.

He accepted a bribe!

How can he call himself a seonbi?

People respected a man possessing a sound *seonbi* spirit regardless of his wealth.

He's a profoundly educated man!

A respectable man indeed.

Today, things haven't changed. People follow and respect upright, straight-shooting and impartial leaders.

A man like him is hard to find these days.

As long as each Korean aspires to live by this *seonbi* spirit,

If all else fails, we must, at least, have the right mentality.

Sure! To avoid becoming fools in front of our kids...

Korea can overcome any obstacle confronting the country.

선비 정신*

Present and future obstacles included.

* Seonbi spirit

This *seonbi* spirit is the force that serves as the gatekeeper to the spirit of modern day Koreans.

Korean Spirit

Seonbi 선비

Spirit 정신

The *seonbi* sprit is very rigid, as what is deemed to be rightful hardly ever changes.

Our decision is absolutely, unequi-vocally right!

If we're not careful here, our egos won't fit through the door!

This is the *choong* mentality at work...

The Koreans need an upgraded, modern seonbi spirit for the 21st century!

As we discussed, due to their different geographical locations,

the Chinese, Koreans and Japanese came to possess very different characteristics.

The differences among continental countries, peninsular countries and island countries apply not only to Asian countries, but also to other countries around the world. Shall we take a look?

Analogy time. If China is the representative continental country in Asia, its counterpart in Europe would be France.

These two countries absorbed various races through a policy of toleration and inclusion.

In Chinese, we say 'Da Tong Zhu Yi'!*

Yes! Tolerance! Conciliation and compromise!

Both countries also absorbed various cultures and made it into their own.

Han culture.

French culture.

* In Korean, Daedongjueui

They are both very proud people.

We're the greatest!

When describing France, the French enjoy using words like 'great' or 'grand.'

La grande nation! (Our great nation!)

This is how we refer to our country.

'La grande armee' refers to the French armed forces.

Where did this pride come from? You could say it arises from the illustrious history and culture of each country.

China is the origin of all Asian culture!

We're the father of all European countries. Look at our history!

At the same time, the people of both countries are very individualistic.

It doesn't really matter who the leader is...

That's right. As long as I'm happy...

They refuse to sacrifice themselves for whatever cause.

Huh? Why me?

Yikes! You're crazy!

Now we can also see many similarities between island countries, e.g., Japan and England.

The people of these two countries suffer in various degrees from xenophobia.

Their cultures developed at a slower pace compared to continental countries.

They had no choice but to accept the cultures of other people.

But they did so only on a selective basis.

Foreign cultures were modified to fit their own purposes.

* Yoidokotori

The greatest threat they faced was internal strife.

So they avoided conflict.

The Japanese don't shake hands. They bow instead.

When the English do a handshake, rarely would you see them doing it firmly and vigorously.

They hold the hand lightly and finish off the handshake without much fanfare.

The people of both countries are very proud.

The British Empire!

Empire of the Sun, Japan!

This pride is attributable to the characteristic of islanders to deify themselves.

Japan, the land of the gods Tenno...

It is a very abstract sense of pride.

Holy, holy!

Those islanders have taken in too much sun again!

Divine!

They avoid extreme behavior and language to reduce the chances of confrontation.

Thanks for all your troubles.

Oh, it's nothing at all!

They also firmly unite to ward off foreign invaders.

United front

This applies whether a foreign country is invading the state itself or the economy. Red tape is everywhere.

Try the office next door.

Try the office next door.

Try the government office.

Ex-port | Govern-ment office | Politician | Business

The group comes before the individual. Each person is accountable to the group.

Mr. Kimura got the promotion!

His peers should all resign.

In Japan, it is not rare for a senior manager of a company gone sour to kill himself, hoping society would forgive him.

The president of the company is in a jam because of my faults. I can't go on...

In times of war, the English nobility rushed to the battlefield, offering their services.

Reporting for duty, sir!

The Count of Kennsington volunteering for frontline battle!

But unthinkable crimes still occur even in Japan where public security is known as being well maintained.

The top news today, a junior high school student murdered a primary school student.

England, in fact, is the home of the infamous hooligans...

arrgg

Why? Under the stifling conditions of an island, pent up energy is bound to explode in some way.

bustle

bustle

Meanwhile, the people of the Balkan peninsula exhibit a temperament that is most similar to that of the Koreans.

The two people share a common history of suffering for thousands of years from constant foreign invasions.

BALKANS
Mongols/Huns
Latin
Arabs
Slavs Mongols Germans
Chinese
Japanese
KOREA

Many different people intermingled on the Balkan peninsula for thousands of years.

Mix of nations

Yugoslavia Serbia Turkey
Bulgaria Rumania
Croatia
Greece Macedonia Albania

But, to this day, each people lives in its own country, having preserved its own unique culture.

Rumania
Serbia
Bulgaria
Macedonia
Albania Greece

Pretty much the same thing the Koreans did to preserve their identity for thousands of years.

The history of my family...

* Family tree

They turned their backs on foreign people in an effort to preserve their racial heritage.

Out-siders not allowed

Of course, this bred enormous pride among such people.

We are a proud people!

They adhered to an orthodoxy that embraced only the fundamental.

Origi-nal
Mixture = hodgepodge
Adaptation, change = sham

A somewhat drastic and extreme characteristic that developed over a difficult history...

and a very stubborn and uncompromising personality are traits shared by the Koreans and the Balkans.

Coke tastes better!
Uh-uh... Pepsi!!

They did whatever they could do to protect their lives, families and property from foreign invaders.

They're coming again!!

A cooperative spirit and strong group orientation are also similar traits shared by these people.

United we stand, divided we fall!

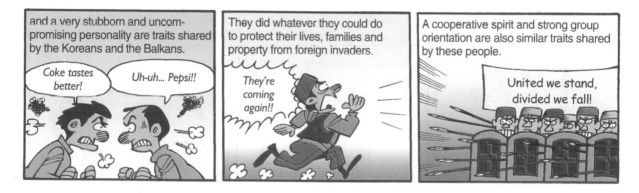

Eventually, peninsular people learned through history that nobody was going to watch out for themselves.

People came to mistrust others.

My life! My family! My property!

It's me or nothing!

It is a temperament that arose from the special circumstances of peninsular countries.

Kicked this way...

Kicked that way...

It was inevitable that peninsular people developed into a 'tough' people.

Only the strong survive!

These resolute individuals united when necessary,

united defense

but, usually, the word 'compromise' was a foreign language and stubbornness a way of life.

Why don't you do as you're told!

Are you the boss? Why are you telling me what to do?

Characterized by a strong sense of individualism, peninsular people can hardly agree on anything!

This side! That side! Over here! Here!

Most of the Balkan countries are agricultural countries.

There are very few people who migrate.

Balkan peninsula

Each individual unites based on his territorial background and bloodline...

Kosovo! Albania! Serbians over here!

But it's a little more complicated in Korea.

Migrating population

Industrialized society

The Koreans instinctively cling to every possible group they can identify with for protection, whether it is based on bloodline, educational background or regional ties.

Educational background

Regional ties

Others

Family ties

Whether it's in Korea or the Balkan peninsula, you'll see that cronyism is alive and well.

M High School, Class of 1988, K Univ., Class of 1992. Born in XX Province, Andong. Kim Lineage.

The Korean People

The Korean Character

• Orthodoxy, egalitarianism and cronyism

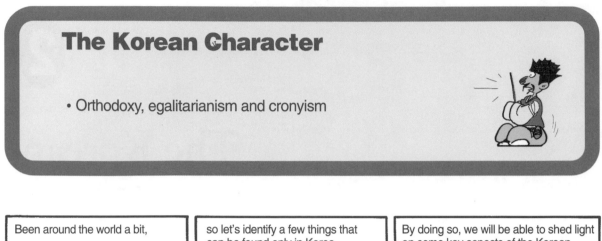

| Been around the world a bit, | so let's identify a few things that can be found only in Korea. | By doing so, we will be able to shed light on some key aspects of the Korean character. |

● **First of all, the endless rows of apartment buildings!**

Hong Kong is known to be packed with apartments, but Hong Kong is just a city. There is no other country in the world like Korea that is covered with sprawling apartment complexes throughout the country, whether it is in a metropolitan area or a rural area.

Incredible! Simply incredible!

© The Chosun Ilbo

62

Think about this. With limited space, if everybody wanted to live in a warm cozy home... What would it take?

Nothing worse than a man without a home!

Moving Center 555-5555

Although you can't smell fresh soil, apartments would be the only alternative.

But no other place in the world has apartment complexes spread across the country like wallpaper.

People live in apartments with the same size, design and layout shared by their neighbors.

17 18

Given that the Koreans cannot stand falling behind others,

Does she think wrapping that dead animal around her neck makes her special?

anything different immediately catches the eyes of neighbors.

Oh boy! They're getting a wide-screen TV!

大型TV 42" PROJECTION TV

Rumors of the new television would then fly all over the apartment complex.

Did you see that new 42-inch wide screen TV?

It's going to be unbearable to see them showing off!

Rumors, words spread like a plague.

Our TV's in perfect condition. Why do you want to buy a new one?

What if your son feels inferior to the next-door neighbor's kid?

Fierce competition ensues...

We're going to get a 42-inch TV!

How about a 53-inch TV!

Umm.. I think 60-inch is the biggest you can buy!

Introduced to the market only a few years ago, refrigerators built for *kimchi* are outselling standard refrigerators.

Kimchi fridge

Standard fridge

People send their kids to all kinds of after-school tutoring programs to keep them ahead of the pack.

English lesson

Piano lesson

School subject lesson

Art lesson

Computer lesson

The Koreans have taken their 'equal profit sharing' mentality to a whole new level, which, in this modern day, has taken on a new name... 'Apartment disease.'

The kid next door goes to tutors after school.

We can't let our child just sit at home and play!

● Walking through the streets of Korea resembles walking through a labyrinth of endless signs. In fiercely competitive Korean society, signs play a crucial role, alerting customers to the location and nature of businesses. Korean signs fight for every inch, having been plastered chaotically on buildings, overlapping in some cases and always looking for the upper hand. A competitive spirit that knows no limit – it's the Korean mentality at work. One must never lose out to a neighbor. This compulsion disfigures the city. Signs on windows... Signs on building walls... Signs posted on rooftops... The signs have taken over.

This sign warfare is also waged by pharmacies that exist to preserve the health of the people.

A pharmacy must make a patient at ease...

Lately, the trend in Korea has been to put up huge signs with bold red letters.

*

I'm blinded!

* Victory Pharmacy

It's the basic Korean mentality at work: I may not be able to win,

but at least I will not fall behind!

I'm not going to be last!

Me, neither!

Me, neither!

If business owners would just compromise a little, they could display elegant and easy-to-read signs for their customers.

Norebang*
3F
Taekwondo
3F
Pediatrician
2F
Physician
2F
Optician 1F

* Singing room

But this isn't quite that easy for the Koreans, as they engage in a sign warfare, battling as if their lives depend on it.

식당*

식당

* Restaurant

● Churches with steeples and red neon crosses...

Nowhere in the world other than in Korea would you find as many churches with steeples! As if there's an unspoken agreement, churches occupying space in commercial buildings maintain steeples on slab roofs. One steeple alone is strange enough to a foreigner, but imagine the sight of three or four steeples on the same rooftop!

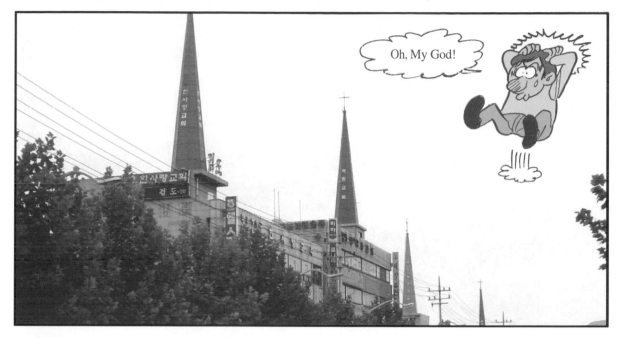

At night, Seoul transforms into a forest of red neon crosses.

Tourists coming to Korea for the first time are befuddled.

In fact, one might even ask:

Is the entire city of Seoul a graveyard?

Why are there so many red crosses!

Christianity forbids the worshipping of idols...

Thou shall not worship idols!

yet Korean churches put up red neon crosses without exception... as if it is the cross itself that matters.

This is another prime example of the Korean temperament.

What others do...

I must do, too!

65

● The extreme nature of student and labor movements.

Although the situation has markedly improved in recent years, whenever demonstrations or strikes break out, the situation often resembles a war zone. Until the 1970s, Japan also faced violent demonstrations in which spears, gas masks, helmets and shields were commonly utilized. Such demonstrations have largely vanished in Japan. In Korea, however, it is not uncommon to still see rocks and Molotov cocktails flying and steel pipes and wooden clubs being wielded in demonstrations.

© The Chosun Ilbo

Whenever there's a demonstration, there's always someone shaving off all of his or her hair.

Why take it out on your hair?

The demonstrators commonly tie red bandanas around their heads and raise their fists in the air, as if there's no tomorrow.

No! No! No!

They break out the drums and gongs...

TANG! TANG! TANG!

They follow the head 'cheerleader' in movements even synchronized swimmers would envy.

Come to your senses!!

Like seasoned professionals, they sing songs, dance and shout slogans in unison.

We shall overcome! We shall overcome!

Foreigners drop their jaws at this sight that can be witnessed only in Korea.

Koreans... *They go all the way...*

Waa *Waa*

● **Nearly 75% of the population is on the go during the Lunar New Year and Chusok (Thanksgiving) holidays.**
Among the 46 million Korean population, 32 million people return to their hometowns during these holidays.
Korea is the only country in the world where as many as 75% of the population hit the roads at the same time.

Special transportation services are put into place during these holidays, and

24-hour live broadcasts of road and traffic conditions are made available.

Korea's probably the only country in the world that places temporary toilets along the congested parts of the highways.

Of course, many Americans and Europeans also travel during the Christmas and Easter season.

But not all of them travel to spend their entire vacation time visiting parents and relatives....

Instead, many people spend vacations at home, resting and relaxing.

What are some other unique Korean characteristics? When something catches on, you'll soon see a whole bunch of it spreading like wild fire.

Victory Norebang*

Passion Norebang

Norebang

Seoul Norebang

Cha Cha Cha Norebang

Unification Norebang

* Norebang: Singing room, Korean equivalent of Karaoke

It's a trait foreigners have a hard time understanding.

Karaoke first made its appearance in Japan during the 1980s,

and its fever soon swept across Japan.

Karaoke

Karaoke 60s Karaoke

Ka ra oke

The *Norebang* was introduced to Korea in the 1990s.

Karaoke

Within three years, tens of thousands of *norebangs* sprouted all over Korea. The rate of penetration was far greater than in Japan.

Sweet dreams are made of this... Who am I to disagree...

Nore-bang   Nore-bang   Nore-bang   Nore-bang   Nore-bang

Within two to three years, tens of thousands of Internet cafés called PC *bang* or PC room, a recent phenomenon, opened all over Korea.

zing   zing
boing   zap   zap

PC
PC Room
PC Room
Internet PC Game Room
Internet
PC room
PC Game Room
PC

And what about teenagers dyeing their hair?

Japanese teenagers started dyeing their hairs in the early 1970s.

Even when this was a popular new look, there were more Japanese teenagers who did not dye their hair.

As late as in the mid 1990s, Korean people thought it was very strange for youths to dye their hair.

What have you done to your hair? You're not a Westerner, you know!

However, today, teenagers who haven't dyed their hair seem to be the minority.

GAP

Oh yes! There's something else you can find only in Korea.

There's a large number of restaurants that stress they're the original thing, or *wonjo*.

Original food for royalty

Authentic Korean food, authentic Japanese food and authentic Chinese food.

Authen-tic	Masan Steamed Fish
Authen-tic	Japanese Food
Authen-tic	Chinese Cuisine

Doesn't stop there. Authentic French, authentic Italian, authentic royal court cuisine...

Authentic French Cuisine La Seine	Authentic Italian Food Toscana	Authentic Korean Food Arirang

They claim their restaurants are where it all started.

Original Jumuleok* Seoul Restaurant
#1 Jumuleok Chunghae
Original Jumuleok Jongno Restaurant

· · · · · · ·

* Pork or beef barbecued with seasoning

Each restaurant claims to be the original.

Other places are copycats!

Look who's talking!

Original Haejang-guk*

Home of the Haejang-guk

* Soup commonly consumed to relieve hangovers

What does it mean to be 'authentic'?

This is sliced radish kimchi made with our great grandmother's recipe from the Joseon period!

Nothing must have been added or changed.

We've made it with grandma's secret recipe!

In other words, the original purity must not have been impaired.

We make our solleongtang* like they did during the Joseon period!

Original seasonings only without any additives!

* Ox-bone soup

Restaurateurs stress they're the original – not some copycat, outsider that has jumped into the game late.

We're the original. Everybody else is a copycat!

Hey! It's not like you're the only one who makes that!

The fact that the Koreans value authenticity and legitimacy is also exemplified by their attitude towards genealogy.

Family Tree

Sure, there are foreigners who are also keenly interested in genealogy.

Was bestowed the title Earl of Nottingham by Henry VII.

FAMILY CHRONO-

70

But in Europe, people tend to bring up the family tree to be pretentious.

As you can see... Uhhum... We are of noble lineage!

Otherwise, in general, most people are unaware of their genealogies.

So, tell me about your family line...

What? Am I a dog you want to breed or something??

In Japan, the Japanese were forbidden to have surnames

Don't even dream about having a surname!!

That's saved for nobles and the samurai!

until the Meiji Restoration in 1868.

There are millions of people in the country with the same names. Distinguish them by giving them surnames.

List of Names

Hence, in most cases, except for the nobility,

I'm Fujiwara.

I'm Daira.

most people aren't concerned about their family lines or genealogies.

We have a genealogical table.

He must come from noble or samurai blood.

It's a completely different case in Korea, where families treasure their books of genealogies like family heirlooms.

Fire!

Save the book of genealogy!

The older members of the families periodically update the missing members of the family tree.

Family Tree of the Hansan Lee Clan

People without genealogical lines are considered 'rootless' families.

We're financially poor, but

we can't accept a son-in-law with no recorded family line!

Look how rigorously people even scrutinize the pedigree of dogs!

Is this dog really a purebred? Does it have a book of genealogy?

What're you talking about? You want me to break out his pedigree??

Saying someone is 'without a family line' is the same as hurling curse words at that person.

How dare you... You don't even exist in a family tree.

This exemplifies how important the Koreans consider orthodoxy and legitimacy.

Why don't you adopt a child?

Without knowing the child's background? How on earth...

* Legitimacy

* King Sejong is considered as one of the greatest rulers in Korean history.

But Prince Chungnyeong's accession to the throne was legitimized by the abdication of his two elder brothers.

The struggle for the throne was fierce throughout the Joseon period.

Power struggles ensued between those in line to inherit the throne and the power figures inside the palace.

Although the Japanese court also stressed tradition, the most qualified person usually ascended to the throne.

The emphasis on legitimacy during the Joseon period is well exemplified by the cold treatment people bestowed on illegitimate sons.

It didn't matter if one was born into the noblest of families if he was the son of a concubine.

He was never treated as a son nor could he ever hold any government posts.

He was discriminated against in the cruelest ways, forbidden to even utter the word 'father.'

The first novel written using the Korean alphabet, *Hangeul*, was 'Hong Gil-dong Jeon.'*

* The Life of Hong, Gil-dong

This novel portrays the hardship and pain of an illegitimate child...

Remnants of this need for legitimacy and orthodoxy can still be found in Korea.

Although society has made many strides since then, you can still see hints of the past showing their faces.

The Koreans like to insist on being legit and to stick to the original plan of things.

Umm... We don't like fakes!

Legitimacy

NO!

They dislike things that stray from the original...

Hybrid!

Poor imitation!

This is a product of the exclusionary behavior of people trying to hold on to their special privileges...

Legitimacy

Holding on to this is the only way I can be authentic!

No longer existing now, there used to be a number of prestigious high schools that everyone aspired to attend.

K High School   S High School

People considered passing the difficult entrance exam as the 'legitimate' way of entering these schools...

You passed!

Rewarded for all your suffering!

These so-called authentic students bullied and alienated transfer students and those filling vacancies.

That loser's transfer garbage!

He didn't even take the entrance exam...

When the government abolished the entrance exam and switched to a lottery system,

You're going to M High School!

the former students who had taken the entrance exam didn't acknowledge the 'lottery' students as fellow alumni.

Lottery system?

That means any idiot can attend our alma mater!

The tradition has ended!

We can't consider these freeloaders to be fellow alumni of the great K High!

Same thing happens in the work place.

There's the new guy.

Didn't you say he got this job without taking the company entrance exam?

He must have someone rooting for him...

The guys at the top must have let him in!

That guy is not legit.

We can't let him into the club.

Infatuation with the original... Reluctance to accommodate change...

These characteristics, of course, are also evident in Korean culture.

The Japanese way of thinking, however, is very different.

As an island country, Japan had no choice but to accept things foreign, whether it was culture or goods...

Why? Someone else invented it anyway!

Rather than preserving the original shape of an import, the Japanese modified it to fit their particular needs.

Compared to the Koreans that stuck, without exception, to the original, whether native or foreign,

the Japanese modified what belonged to others, making it suitable for themselves.

The Japanese leave a lot of room for change, making practical revisions to suit their needs.

The different mentalities are also exemplified by the way the Koreans and the Japanese read Chinese characters.

Chinese characters are used in both Korea and Japan.

The Japanese have different ways of reading the same Chinese character.

> Reading Chinese characters the Japanese way is practically impossible for a foreigner!

There are two ways of reading Chinese characters in Japan. One way is the phonetic approach, *Onyomi*, the phonetic reading of the Chinese characters.

Kuruma

Sha

Hikoki

Shinkansen

And the other way is the semantic approach, *Kunyomi*, the semantic reading of the Chinese characters.

男	犬	竹
Otoko (Man)	Inu (Dog)	Take (Bamboo tree)

酒	組	朝
Sake (Wine)	Kumi (Gathering)	Asa (Morning)

It's confusing when the Japanese switch back and forth between the two pronunciation methods to suit their needs.

> Phonetic reading + Semantic reading

What makes matter worse, they also have different ways of pronouncing the same word.

居 酒 屋 (Pub)

i saka ya

(Phonetic) (Semantic) (Semantic)

Ordinarily, should be read sake but it's actually pronounced saka.

There are plenty of examples where *Onyomi* and *Kunyomi* are mixed.

> Just shoot me now!

● ○
番 組
(Ban gumi)
Program

○ ●
消 印
(Geshi in)
Postmark

○ ●
見 本
(Mi hon)
Sample

○ ●
切 符
(Ki(t) ppu)
Ticket

● ●
東 京
(To kyo)

○ ○
横 浜
(Yoko hama)

● ○
団 子
(Tang ko)

○ ●
赤 門
(Aka mon)
Red gate

From time to time, even the Japanese themselves get confused.

> How do you read this?

> Geez... I'm not sure either!

Mixing and interchanging the phonetic and semantic readings—this is a very difficult task for foreigners trying to learn Japanese and its Chinese characters.

> That's hunseng?

> No... It's sinagawa.

品川

The Chinese are also sticklers for traditions.

> Chinese culture's the legitimate East Asian culture!

However, China was plagued by countless wars throughout its history.

argg waag

Examples of Simplified Chinese Characters

① Alteration of archaic letters	② Reduction or elimination of parts	③ Preservation of only certain parts	④ Change of complicated parts to symbols	⑤ Creation of new characters
气 ← 氣	标 ← 標	声 ← 聲	戏 ← 戲	毕 ← 畢
从 ← 從	竞 ← 競	广 ← 廠	鸡 ← 鷄	华 ← 華
车 ← 車	单 ← 單	习 ← 習	汉 ← 漢	尘 ← 塵
万 ← 萬	冲 ← 沖	乡 ← 鄉	岁 ← 歲	宝 ← 寶

This wasn't accepted by the Koreans, who, of course, emphasize legitimacy and orthodoxy.

What! Change the original thing because it's difficult?

As a result, the Koreans still use the original Chinese characters...

The simplified characters have nothing to do with us!

ORIGINAL

We'd be breaking a tradition of thousands of years if we change the form of Chinese characters.

TRADITION

Unlike Japanese, the Korean language does not have a semantic method of reading Chinese characters.

Cheon* O

Haneul* X

天 Heaven

There is only one way of reading Chinese characters—pronouncing the sound of each character precisely

Earth **ji**
Yellow **hwang**
Heaven **cheon**
Dark **hyun**

There are only a few exceptions to this rule.

Exceptions

金 pronounced 'Gim' or 'Geum'
金永秀 Gim Yeong-su (person's name)
金剛山 Geumgang-san (Mt. Geumgang)

* Korean word for the 'heavens'
* Phonetic reading of the Chinese character for the 'heavens'

If these few exceptions are kept in mind, there shouldn't be problems reading Chinese characters in conjunction with Korean.

Memorize these few exceptions to the rule.

樂山樂水=nak-san-nak-su X
　　　　yo-san-yo-su O
內人=nae-in X
　　　na-in O

70% of the Korean language is derived from Chinese words but only one pronunciation is recognized for each character.

Je-gong?

In Korean that could mean... 'offer' 'offerings' 'mastery of the air,' 'gentleman,' etc.

A homonym, when spoken or written only in the Korean alphabet, may at times be confusing because the equivalent Chinese character meaning would be different depending on the context.

정의 = 正義, 定擬, 定議, 定義,
　　　正意, 正倚, 征衣, 廷議,
　　　淨衣, 情誼, 情義, 精意

Sometimes, sticking to traditions and the original of things...

Original

causes its fair share of headaches.

Can't break through to the other side!!

Switching topics... they say It's hard to make friends in Korea.

Why? Due to Confucian traditions, it is important to be aware of hierarchy and rank in Korean society.

Age | Title   etc., etc.

It is easy to became acquainted, but difficult to become bosom buddies, with another person.

What does age have to do with anything? It's everything. A wide gap in age prevents people from becoming friends.

How old are you?? Still wet behind the ears, and you're trying to be an equal?

What about differences in job titles? Chalk it up as another obstacle...

Hey chief... Can we be friends?

Have you completely lost your mind? What do you take me for?

Generational differences are another obstacle...

Sunbae-nim! (Dear senior)

Hubae! (Junior)

In the West, age, status and generation gaps can be transcended in establishing friendships.

Hey Peter!

Hi, Charlie!

However, in Korea, it's difficult to transcend such barriers and form relationships.

You mocking me?

How dare you informally address a seonbae!

Friendships can only be established when various factors are relatively equal...

Similar in age...

Similar titles...

A group of persons can remain as friends as long as they maintain similar titles.

Next round's on me!

Cool!

However, if one of them should move up high in a promotion...

or down in a demotion...

• baekbu (uncle, father's older brother) • sukbu (father's younger brother) • dangjil (male cousin's son) • dongseo (brother-in-law)
• jahyeong (older sister's husband) • gomo (aunt, father's sister) • imo (maternal aunt) • dangsuk (father's male cousin)
• cheohyeong (sister-in-law) • maehyeong (older sister's husband) • saengjil (nephew) • danggomo (grandfather's niece on the brother's side) • dangsukbu (father's male cousin) • jabu (daughter-in-law) • cheojae (wife's younger sister) • maejae (younger sister's husband) • ijongsachon (cousin by maternal aunt)

Let's now break down the family relationship. The unit representing the distance between relatives is 'chon.'

Chon = Degree of Kinship

A husband and wife are 0 chon apart, as a couple is considered one body and soul. Parents and children are 1 chon or 1 degree in distance.

Father — 0 — chon — Mother

1 chon

What about the relationship between siblings?

Mother — Father

1 chon | 1 chon

Elder son | Younger son

1 chon + 1 chon = 2 chon (siblings)

What about your father's older and younger brothers? Follow the map...

Father — Older brother (2 chon)
— Younger brother (2 chon)

1 chon

Me

1 chon + 2 chon = 3 chon (Uncle)

What about you and your grandfather or grandmother?

Grandfather — Father

1 chon (Father and son)

Me — Father

1 chon

Grandfather 1 chon + 1 chon = 2 chon

The grandfather maintains a 2 chon kinship with me.

Time for a quick quiz—how distantly related a chon are you with your father's older brother's grandson?

Me ⟷ Father = 1 chon (father and son)

Father ⟷ Father's older brother = 2 chon (brothers)

Father's older brother ⟷ Grandson = 2 chon

1 chon + 2 chon + 2 chon = 5 chon

Answer: 5 chon

Now, there are different titles for different levels and degrees of kinship (chon) in a Korean family. It may look complicated, but the Koreans must be aware of these titles.

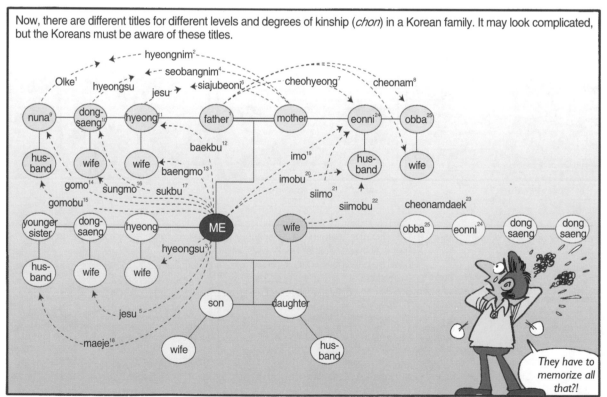

They have to memorize all that?!

1. for women: brother's wife, i.e., sister-in-law 2. husband's older sister 3. for men: older brother's wife, i.e., sister-in-law 4. husband's younger brother 5. for men: younger brother's wife 6. husband's older brother 7. wife's older sister 8. wife's brother, older and younger 9. a man's older sister 10. younger brother(or sister) 11. older brother 12. father's older brother, elder uncle 13. elder aunt 14. aunt on the father's side 15. uncle, aunt's husband 16. aunt, wife of father's younger brother 17. father's younger brother 18. for men: younger sister's husband 19. aunt, mother's sister 20. maternal aunt's husband 21. husband's imo, aunt on the mother's side 22. siimo's husband 23. wife of cheonam, brother-in-law 24. for women: elder sister 25. for women: elder brother

The World Record Parade

The Koreans are the most _____ people in the world.

* Spicy shredded soup

* Hot pepper paste

The Koreans, who take eating spicy food to the extreme,

Any hotter and my mouth or stomach will explode.

also take drinking to the extreme.

Whiskey imports = #1 in Asia
Cognac imports = #2 in Asia
Soju* consumption = 4 billion bottles per year

* Korean equivalent of vodka

The younger people show some restraint and generally know when to call it a night.

You don't want anymore?

No, I have to work tomorrow.

But many people in the older generations have to go all the way.

Let's call it a night. It's already our fourth bar.

What are you talking about? One more glass! Just one more!

They go from one drinking spot to another getting absolutely tanked.

1st dive → 2nd hole → 3rd cove → 4th spot

They pass around one cup, signifying the 'all for one and one for all' mentality.

Take my glass!

Drink and pass it along!

'If I drink, you have to drink.' This mentality may be traced to the 'egalitarianism' prevailing in Korean society.

I can't drink! Really...

Everybody else's drinking but you! Take it or die!

There is also a drink called 'poktanju' (poktan = bomb, ju = drink) (known as boilermaker in the West) which is made by dropping a glass full of whiskey into a glass full of beer.

Whiskey
Poktanju
Beer

The poktanju was 'invented' by soldiers who, until recently, governed Korean society.

cheers!

The drink is indeed like a bomb because it levels whoever it comes into contact with!

mommy

Whether it is regarding food or alcohol, the Koreans display this extreme personality.

Take it to the end!

crash!

Doesn't end here... when it comes to swearing. Oh man! Cover your ears!

We're the world champs in swearing.

Shall we look at what some people consider as the most important aspect of society?

RELIGION

宗教·信仰

Along with the folk religions of Korea, add Christianity, Buddhism, Confucianism and Islam to the mix.

I believe in you, Father

Return to the Amitabha!

Confucius!

Virgin Mary...

Allah!

KOREA

Divine spirits!

Korean Christianity especially has some surprisingly unique elements not found anywhere else in the world today. Not found in the history of the world for that matter.

UNBELIEVABLE!

Korean Chris-tianity

Christianity was introduced to Korea in the form of Catholicism during the 17th century.

Yi Su-gwang

Ji-Bong-Yu-Seol*

Book of Catholic ideology written in Chinese characters by missionary Matteo Ricci

At the time, when Catholicism entered the country, the Koreans didn't consider it as a religion. They merely considered it as a Western institution.

Westerners think the world is round.

Those ignorant fools.

As Catholicism started to gain a larger following, however, during the 19th century, the government started to suppress it.

What? Jesus is the king of kings? Treasonous Catholic!

Many churches were formed during the Japanese occupation of Korea(1910-1945). They made significant contributions to Korea's independence movement.

People of Korea must wake up!

Keep knocking at the door and it will open. Till we find our freedom.

But Christianity (Protestantism) spread in earnest throughout Korea...

Believe and attain salvation ('guwon,' in Korean)

What?? Will you give me 9 (=gu) won?

as the U.S. military rolled into town after Korea's liberation from Japan in 1945.

Jesus Christ

US

Oh, my god!

Merry Christmas!

??

Christianity's explosion happened during the 1970s

Bang

when Korea's economy started to develop at a rapid pace.

Korean Economy

$

Korean Christianity

In other words, it has only been three decades since Christianity has become a mainstream religion in Korea.

Growth of Korean Christianity

1945 '55 '65 '75 '85 '95

Currently, there're at least 15 million Christians (including Catholics) living in Korea.

It's impossible to get an exact count!

That's nearly 35% of the entire Korean population. Astonishing to say the least.

1 Protestantism and Catholicism
2 Buddhism
3 Others

Take a look at these numbers—over 50,000 churches spread across the country and over 10,000 churches in Seoul alone. The most in Asia.

The five largest protestant churches in the world are in Seoul!

That's really a church?

In a span of only 30 years, nearly 35% of the Korean population have become Christians!

That's a world record! Definitely the first time in history that has happened!

I'm surprised, too.

Heaven ↗

In the history of humankind, this kind of phenomenon has happened only in Korea.

In Europe, it took several hundreds of years for Christianity to spread.

Wake up! It's the 8th century!

You still believe in those pagan gods?

Christianity crossed over into Japan from Portugal nearly 100 years before it hit the shores of Korea.

However, Christians now make up less than 1% of the Japanese population.

Hey, you observe Christmas?

No, it's just a holiday. There's no religious meaning.

Before Christianity could spread into China, the socialist government declared that religion was a mere opium of the people.

Religion... The opium of the people!

Karl Marx

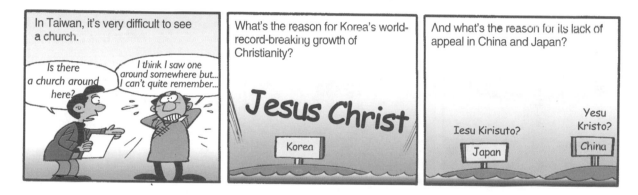

In Taiwan, it's very difficult to see a church.

Is there a church around here?

I think I saw one around somewhere but... I can't quite remember...

What's the reason for Korea's world-record-breaking growth of Christianity?

Jesus Christ

Korea

And what's the reason for its lack of appeal in China and Japan?

Iesu Kirisuto?

Japan

Yesu Kristo?

China

China has a countless number of religions.

With a population of 1.3 billion, *there're all kinds of religions here.*

Religion was suppressed in China after the Communists took over.

No god's going to deliver you! Socialism will!

Most of its religions supplicate for personal and family happiness.

Please let me make a lot of money and stay healthy.

Fortune-Wishing Faith

The huge difference between Christianity in Korea and Japan is attributable to the difference in their religious foundations.

Oh, Abeoji (Father)

Kamisama (Goddess)...

Clap Clap Clap

Japan's native religion is animism...

animism

Originated from the Latin word *anima*
Anima: Soul, life, to blow in life
Animal: Living organism
Animation: = Moving picture

In other words, the Japanese believed that all things in existence have souls.

Soul of the wind

Soul of a tree   Soul of a rock

They believed rocks, trees, grass, animals... all existence for that matter had souls. Hence, all beings are deities.

rock   grass   mountain

river   ocean   forest

Very polytheistic in nature. Needless to say, there're many so-called gods running around in Japan.

bustle bustle

bustle ↑
sound of the gods

There are over 8 million 'gods' in Japan because of its religious roots being grounded in animism.

The Japanese soldiers who died during World War II have been enshrined at the Yasukuni Shrine. In other words, they have been deified.

軍曹
松本浩一

Thus, polytheism, which is rooted in animism, is the foundation of all Japanese religions.

Japanese religions

Poly-theism

Animism

To make a long story short, this all boiled down to Shintoism, with Amaterasu-O-mi-kami as the founding goddess.

Shintoism has become Japan's basic religion.

Animism   Polytheism

Influence of Buddhism

Japanese gods

Japanese legends

Amaterasu-O-mi-kami → Shintoism

Monotheistic religions didn't stand a chance in Japan.

There's only one God.

Nonsense!

Meanwhile, the native religions of Korea started from shamanism. It's the opposite from Japan.

Shamanism

사이비 종교

Shamanism started among the natives living in northern Siberia and spread across the Far East, to places like Mongolia and the Korean peninsula.

It's a mysterious and vast world...

Whenever spring comes, the flowers bloom and plants start to sprout...

Contrary to animism that believed everything had souls...

All these events are the doings of some invisible, omnipotent, omniscient and spiritual being...

An absolute being! Some kind of divinity exists! I'm sure of it...

Thunder

Shamans made contact with this god, as well as the spirits of the dead.

Your average Joe from the streets can't meet such a divine existence.

Only a few select, sacred and holy people can meet such a god.

They called the spirits from the dead and prophesied about the future, good or bad.

O' divine one! Let our harvest be bountiful this year!

Let misfortune fall far away from this village!

The shamans were in constant contact with these divine and dead spirits...

Umm... I have a license to do business with the spirits!

My name... 'mudang' (Shaman)...

rattle rattle

In short, the shamanism belief was that there is only one supreme being governing nature.

Animism → All beings come with souls

Shamanism → One great divine being

That's totally ridiculous!

Although rudimentary in nature, shamanism and the monotheistic ideology have a lot in common.

Shamanism → Monotheistic ideology

Mixed bag of Gods

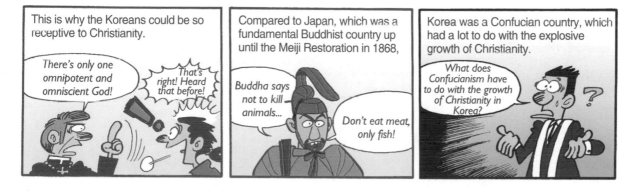

This is why the Koreans could be so receptive to Christianity.

There's only one omnipotent and omniscient God!

That's right! Heard that before!

Compared to Japan, which was a fundamental Buddhist country up until the Meiji Restoration in 1868,

Buddha says not to kill animals...

Don't eat meat, only fish!

Korea was a Confucian country, which had a lot to do with the explosive growth of Christianity.

What does Confucianism have to do with the growth of Christianity in Korea?

Confucianism emphasizes order in the present life and moral principles.

Devotion to country!

Filial piety to your parents! Love to your siblings!

Loyalty to friends!

It is a religion that does not focus on the afterlife, as what is important is this present world.

There's no need to think about what happens after death. Man returns to nature... He turns into dust.

Now... humankind has always been afraid of death.

What happens after I die?

Am I born again into this world?

Or is this it?

Naturally, people hoped for an eternal life in a happy place.

Does everything end here?

Is there any way I can die without pain and live forever? Is that too much to ask for?

The Japanese have eased their worries about the afterlife through Buddhism.

Oh, Buddha...

Buddha has promised us nirvana...

But for the Koreans, Confucianism did not address their worries about the afterlife.

Will being faithful and devoted guarantee me a spot in heaven?

Oh silly one! Do you attach conditions to your faithfulness?

Just imagine how appealing Christianity must have been! It promised heaven and eternal life.

I will make you lie down in green pastures...

The kingdom of heaven is yours! I shall give you eternal peace and life!

After working day and night, and becoming fatigued and exhausted,

Life is so hard! What's all this suffering for?

I commit sins, too, against my will.

listening to the words of God gave them strength and comfort.

Knock and the door will open!

Believe! The Father will forgive you of all your sins!

For this and other reasons, Christianity was quickly and warmly received in Korea.

Oh Lord!

I believe!

Hallelujah!

As mentioned earlier, in less than 30 years, we're looking at a country where 35% of the people profess to be Christians!

Do you believe in the Father? Without any doubts?

I believe!

Amen!

The unprecedented increase in the number of Christians in Korea is another prime example of the extreme nature of the Koreans who are accustomed to achieving quick results.

Give everything you have to building the house of God!

Amen!

Well, just how extreme are the ideologies of the Koreans?

IDEOLOGY
思想·理念

The first socialist country was born after the Bolshevik Revolution in 1917.

For over 70 years, ideological conflicts plagued the world.

Capitalism and communism are the opposites of each other... like water and vinegar.

Korean capitalism is...

Korean capitalism

the most extreme form of capitalism, exemplified by the chaebol!

재벌*

Chaebol*

* Conglomerates

What about North Korea?

North Korean Communism

Although nearly all the communist countries have fallen, the North Koreans still cling to the most extreme form of Stalinism...

스탈린주의

STALINISM

Devotion!

Won't change even if I die!

No way! Never going to convert!

In the name of Stalinism, dissenters in North Korea are quelled by force.

Oops...

A secret police force keeps the people under constant surveillance.

One all-powerful dictator acts like an emperor.

Allegiance!

Long live the Great Leader!

North Korea is a totalitarian state, an egregiously undemocratic and dictatorial nation.

Refusing to obey the Dear Leader's orders

is an act of treason against the party.

Unconditional obedience

North Korea has cut all ties with the West.

Restricted Area

After the division of Korea, North Korea stubbornly adhered to a policy of self-reliance... becoming the most isolated country in the world.

We're very happy here, even if there's no food on the table!

Juche* Ideology

North Korea

* Self-reliance

Kim Il Sung became the ruler of North Korea in 1945.

Is that Kim Il Sung?

They say so.

He ruled North Korea for nearly 50 years until his death in 1994.

Hurray!

Long live Father Leader comrade Kim Il Sung

Hurrar!

He is recorded in history as a dictator who stayed in power longer than any other dictator in history.

Kim Il Sung	1945~1994 (49 years)
Enver Hoxha	(Albanian dictator) 1946~1985 (39 years)
Nicolae Ceausescu	(Rumanian dictator) 1960~1989 (29 years)
Joseph Stalin	(Soviet Union) 1924~1953 (29 years)

In other socialist countries, when a dictator dies or is ousted from power,

he usually becomes the subject of bitter criticism.

That tyrant's the root of our country's woes!

Let's look at Stalin who ruled the Soviet Union with an iron hand for 30 years...

Soon after Stalin's death, his successor Nikita Khrushchev denounced Stalin as a 'dictator.' Stalin was posthumously stripped of all of his honor.

Look at Mao Zedong (1893-1976), the leader of China's communist revolution.

After his death, his wife Jiang Qing was convicted and executed as being one of the four ringleaders of the Cultural Revolution.

All's in vain without my husband.

However, things have been different in North Korea. Even after Kim Il Sung's death, the people continue to worship him, as if he were a god.

His love is endless!

Oh, comrade leader!

On the other side of the border, the South Koreans followed the road towards democracy.

Capitalism in Korea also went to the farthest of extremes... typical for Koreans.

It is a country where one person owns and controls huge conglomerate groups,

for which he makes all the decisions, acting very much like an emperor in his own right.

Do it!

Yes sir!

The top 10 conglomerates in Korea are all chaebols. Korea's a conglomerate-based capitalistic country.

Samsung Group	Chaebol	
LG Group	Chaebol	
	Chaebol	
Hyundai Group	Chaebol	

You can find many cases in capitalist countries where one family runs a company... or two...

It's a family business.

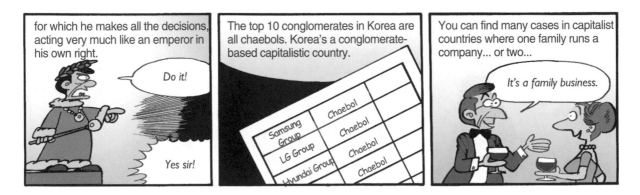

It's rare, however, to find the largest conglomerates controlled by a few families...

From ramen noodles to missiles! We make them all!

Chaebol Republic

In these conglomerates, the chaebol owner passes down management powers to his son.

I hand this over to you. You run it!

Management

Passing ownership control of a conglomerate group of companies to one's children, grand children and so forth is something unthinkable in other countries.

The CEO's elected at the shareholders' meeting.

Shareholders' Meeting

Thus, the Korean economy is characterized by an unusual 'patrimonial chaebol capitalism system.'

Only possible in Korea.

Patrimonial Chaebol Capitalism

The owner of a conglomerate is no different than an emperor.

Whether management powers over large conglomerates are passed on to one's son,

or whether control of the state is

passed on to one's son,

Father

Patrimony → Son | Power · Control

fundamentally, South and North Korea aren't very different.

If there's a difference, in North Korea, the father passed on an entire country to his son,

Country

whereas in South Korea, the chaebol owner passes on his conglomerate, which is like a mini kingdom, to his son.

Management power

This extreme family-oriented ideology,

My eldest son, it's your turn to watch over the clan!

as evidenced by the shift in power from father to son,

Nobody to trust but family!

and the vertical relationship whereby power or property is passed down from father to son,

and the strong patriarchal system in which inheritance is conditioned on absolute obedience,

Since you've given up your studies in business administration, I've decided to turn the company over to your younger brother.

all exemplify the extreme temperament of the Korean people, whether they pursue capitalism or communism.

The Koreans have shown the world unparalleled examples of what

could be the products of their extreme nature.

Let's turn to another topic. How about Korean politics?

POLITICS
政治

If you think of the country as a car, politics would be the steering wheel.

Country

The steering wheel determines the direction in which the car will move.

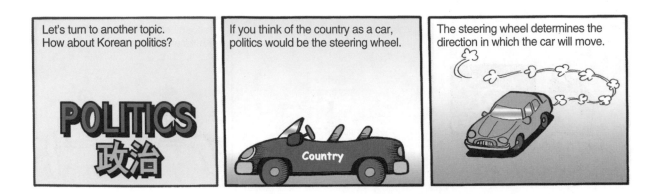

In the case of airplanes and trains with many passengers...

the plane or train moves depending on maneuvers made by the pilot or conductor, respectively.

The lives of those on board depend on them.

That's why you see ambitious people jumping into politics.

I will devote my life for the people...for this great nation!

Yeah buddy...

Politics can be very complicated...

Each country has its own unique political circumstances.

History

Domestic realties

Public sentiment

International situation

Regionalism

Others

The more developed a country, the more stable is its politics...

Vroom

Stability

The more undeveloped a country, the more unstable is its politics... so its people are bound to suffer.

Hey, watch out!

thump clunk

thump clunk

Instability

But politics is a people-intensive business,

There're some people lower than us out there running the show!

woof!

Like other aspects of Korean society, Korean politics also possesses a degree of extremity that can be hardly found anywhere else in the world.

I will never understand that country.

KOREA

Let's address three examples, starting with Korean democracy.

DEMOCRACY OF KOREA

The concept of democracy was first introduced to Korea in 1945 at the time of Korea's liberation from Japan.

Democracy!

Huh?

Although the Korean independence was gained through another country, the U.S.,

---

the passion for democracy burned inside the Korean people.

Having democracy bloom in Korea is like... having a rose bloom in a bed of garbage.

In the 1950s, people looked down on us.

After many revolutions and struggles,

June 29th
Adoption of direct elections

Democra-tization!

Freedom!

May 18th
Gwangju Democratic Movement

No dictators!

April 19th
Student Uprising

---

unquestionably, Korea has now established itself as a democratic country.

There's still work to be done though...

민주주의*

* Democracy

The French Revolution erupted in 1789.

Thereafter, other advanced countries struggled for at least 150 years before achieving democracy.

Anti-revolutionary forces

Revolutionary forces

But it took Korea only 50 years to get to this stage of democracy!

Democracy

If there's a country with a national income level similar to Korea's that has achieved democracy this rapidly, step aside please!

This is a prime example of that Korean mentality of going all the way, finishing what you have started.

Second example. Korean presidents.

The Republic of Korea was established in 1948...

Founding of the Government of the Republic of Korea August 15, 1948

As of 2002, Korea has had eight elected presidents so far.

One* was indirectly elected in a gym...

* Chun Doo Hwan

All of the seven former presidents have,

Park Chung Hee

Roh Tae Woo

Chun Doo Hwan

Kim Young Sam

Rhee Syngman

Yun Po Son

Choi Kyu Ha

without exception, experienced misfortune before or after leaving office.

The Fate of the Former Presidents:
Rhee: Died in exile
Yun and Choi: Resigned under coercion
Park: Assassinated by his intelligence chief
Chun and Roh: Incarcerated for corruption and sedition
Kim: Disgraced by financial crisis

Bang!

It's so appalling, neighboring Japanese reporters even said:

There's no other country in the world whose leaders have endlessly been subject to indignity!

Unfortunately, what this says is that the Koreans haven't had a leader they could truly respect.

How did the president become such a loser?

However, it's probably fair to say that, instead of these gentlemen not having been presidential material,

I mean... He must have had something. He was elected by the people...

there was just a lack of trust and respect for them on the part of the Korean people.

Give me a break! He ignored the will of the people and did what he wanted with the power!

Looking at the seven former presidents, we get some sense of

Not one president left office with the respect of the people.

the extreme and drastic nature of Korean politics.

Because we've been through so much in our history, maybe we're asking for too much from our leaders.

No, no... That's not it! Honesty is all we want!

Third example. The so-called 'Three Kims.'

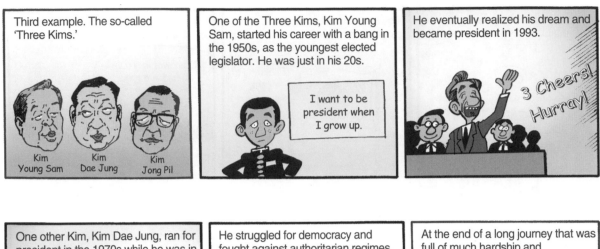

Kim Young Sam

Kim Dae Jung

Kim Jong Pil

One of the Three Kims, Kim Young Sam, started his career with a bang in the 1950s, as the youngest elected legislator. He was just in his 20s.

I want to be president when I grow up.

He eventually realized his dream and became president in 1993.

3 Cheers! Hurray!

One other Kim, Kim Dae Jung, ran for president in the 1970s while he was in his 40s.

It's time for a young man in his 40s to lead this country!

He struggled for democracy and fought against authoritarian regimes.

Kidnapped in Japan

Accused of high treason

Accused of promoting anti-gov't organizations

Accused of being pro-communist

At the end of a long journey that was full of much hardship and heartaches... and even a death sentence...

You are sentenced to death!

bang bang bang

he eventually became president in 1998 and even won the Nobel Peace Prize in 2001...

NOBEL

The third Kim, Kim Jong Pil, made his appearance on the political stage as a key member of the May 16 coup d'etat in 1961 which brought Park Chung Hee to power.

On several occasions, he served as prime minister and ran for president.

Only the president is above me.

夕日照西天

He played an important role in forming a coalition government that brought about a peaceful transfer of power in 1998.*

We won!

Political power

Even after 40 years, he's still a major mover and shaker behind the Korean political scene.

I'm old school!

For a parliamentary cabinet system!

For conservative ideals!

Our purpose here is not to pass judgment on the Three Kims.

* His coalition partner was Kim Dae Jung.

These gentlemen dominated Korean politics for nearly 30 years...

I am so tired of the three Kims...

1970s | 1980s | 1990s | 21st C

using their hometowns as their political bases...

This is my hometown!

J.P. Kim
Chungcheong provinces

D.J. Kim
Jeolla provinces

Y.S. Kim
Gyeongsang provinces

They took advantage of the regionalism existing among these areas, becoming the respective leader of each such area.

It's a Chungcheong man's turn to become president!

A Gyeongsang man for president again!

No more discrimination against the Jeolla people!

JP YS DJ

So-called faction politics is entrenched in the political scene,

Your royal highness... no I mean... Your honorable party chief...

Salutations!

which enable the three Kims to still exert a strong influence on Korean politics.

The Jeolla vote...

Chungcheong vote + Jeolla vote> Gyeongsang vote!

Unite under me!

K K K

KKK...?

You won't find a phenomenon like this in any other, especially democratic, country in the world, where

Power comes from the people!

Don't make me laugh. That's election time mumbo jumbo!

regional leaders, with the backing of loyal regional supporters,

We don't expect anything from our faction leader...

Yeah, right...

remain at the apex of power for so long.

Korea

Three Kims Republic

Now, in North Korea, the father and son, Kim Il Song and Kim Jong Il, have ruled the country for more than 50 years.

North Korea

The Kim Empire

You can see the extreme nature of the Koreas popping up in politics as well, right?

Four Kims are dominating the Korean peninsula!

???

JI YS DJ JP
K K K K

Yes, at least South Korea is a democratic country where all people are equal...

Everyone's equal!

Egalitarian democratic society

But, there's still a strong hierarchical power structure in place, a system hardly different from a monarchy.

You have the boss above the regional king makers and the king makers below the boss!

An emperor-like president!

Hierarchical power structure

This kind of vertical power structure doesn't stop at politics.

Replace those cabinet ministers who don't listen!

Yes, Your Majesty!

It's also prevalent in business, government and even in the family.

Do as you're told!

Yes, Mr. Chairman!

It has become an obstacle to the realization of a true democracy.

If an elder person says it's right, it's right! What do you know?

The Korean people have endlessly struggled to establish a democratic society...

Overthrow the dictator!

We want democracy!

They possess a 'horizontal' way of thinking

As the Joseon Dynasty fell, so did the nobles...

Korea's an egalitarian society.

based on the ideal that everyone is equal.

The president, cabinet members and assembly members...

... are all servants of the people!

But there still exist 'vertical' (hierarchical) elements in society.

Why is he abusing his power like that?

Does he think he's the king or something?

So the people have grown cynical about political and social affairs,

Fine! Do whatever you want!

and have lost faith in their leaders.

I thought he might be different but he's the same old story...

We have absolutely no luck when it comes to leaders!

What's the point here? What's the biggest problem facing Korea?

Hey! Drive properly!

Shut up!

clunk
clunk

It's the collision of the vertical (hierarchical) social structure and the horizontal (egalitarian) way of thinking.

Social structure

Way of thinking

Crash

The only solution to this problem is the achievement of a true, genuine democracy.

Progress of democracy

Social structure

Way of thinking

Okay. Let's now turn our attention to the Korean economy.

ECONOMY 經濟

People often use the expression 'miracle' when talking about a country's economy.

Miracle of the Rhein River!

Miraculous rise of the Japanese economy!

The representative cases of miraculous economic recoveries have to be the losers of World War II.

... Germany and Japan...

But the nature of the Korean economy's miraculous rise is without comparison.

THE MIRACLE OF THE KOREAN ECONOMY

Let's first address the German and Japanese situations. World War II reduced Germany and Japan to ashes.

Let's take this huge sumo wrestler as an example. If he were knocked out by a stronger opponent, he may fall,

but with proper care and a couple of good meals, he'd be back on his feet in no time.

It would only be a matter of time before he's stomping away again in that ring.

The same can be said for the economies of Germany and Japan. Yes, they were knocked out after waging war against the rest of the world.

Let's take over the world!

However, the two countries were economic powerhouses to begin with.

And they did not become prosperous and powerful nations overnight.

Road to wealth and strength

In the case of Germany, it was a weak European country up until the 19th century.

Shooo little one! Go play with the others!

France   Germany

The German people constantly suffered from hunger.

growl...

Potatoes were distributed to the German people during the 18th century to feed the starving people.

Decent taste... Not to mention there're tons of it!

We must distribute this to the people and stop the starvation.

This all changed in 1870 when Germany defeated France, then a world-class power, in the Franco-German War.

This was the beginning of the rise of Germany.

We surrender!

Germany became unified in 1871.

We proclaim the German Second Reich!

With frightening vigor, the Germans started to build up their industrial and military machine.

We'll become a wealthy nation

Wealthy Country Strong Army

and maintain a killer army!!

Iron Chancellor Bismarck said,

England and France have already colonized most of the outside world.

If we can't make advances into these territories...

the only way we can become a powerful nation is by beating them in knowledge and science!

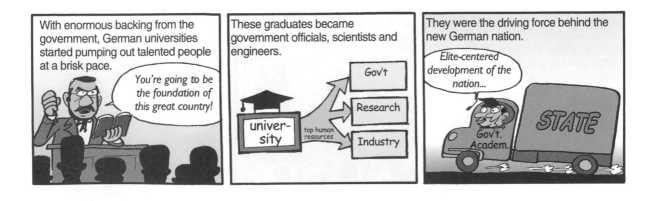

With enormous backing from the government, German universities started pumping out talented people at a brisk pace.

You're going to be the foundation of this great country!

These graduates became government officials, scientists and engineers.

university

top human resources

Gov't

Research

Industry

They were the driving force behind the new German nation.

Elite-centered development of the nation...

Gov't. Academ.

STATE

Based on this national strength and advanced level of science and technology,

Germany was able to stand up quickly after being knocked out in World War I.

Economic resurgence!

Science Technology

In fact, Germany emerged as the strongest country in Europe before World War II.

Bring it on, brother!

But, of course, they lost again in World War II.

You dare try again?

K.O.

USA

Once again, however, with their large pool of talent and highly advanced level of science and technology,

Talent

Skill

coupled with the diligence and frugality of the German people,

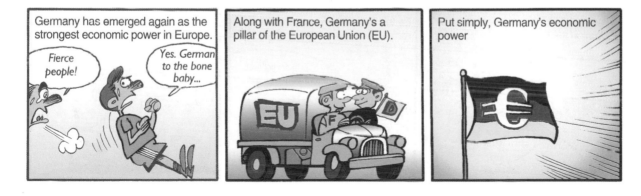

Germany has emerged again as the strongest economic power in Europe.

Fierce people!

Yes. German to the bone baby...

Along with France, Germany's a pillar of the European Union (EU).

EU

F

D

Put simply, Germany's economic power

€

is a product of having strenuously worked towards building itself over a period of 150 years since the late 19th country.

Rome wasn't built in a day!

D

Japan's case is no different.

¥

Up until the mid 19th century, Japan was an isolated island country in the Far East.

They say there's this weird country in the Far East.

Where the people eat their fish raw, right?

Admiral Perry made his way to Japan in 1853.

Open up or I'll shove this down your throat!

Japan was forced to open its doors.

All right... I'll open it!

The Meiji Restoration in 1868 changed the Japanese from head to toe.

They changed the political, economic and military systems of the country. The new systems were modeled after those in the West.

Based on a wealthy country, strong army policy, Japan was able to build up its national strength.

In less than 30 years, the Japanese defeated China in a war.

Sino-Japanese War 1894-1895

K-O...

They shocked the world again by defeating the Russians a decade later.

Russo-Japanese War 1904

By this time, Japan had joined the ranks of world powers.

Konnichiwa!

In 1910, Japan annexed Korea. The Joseon Dynasty was overthrown.

This is our land!

Korean peninsula

The Japanese made a whole lot of money by exporting goods to European countries waging World War I.

Keep fighting! Keep it up!

MADE IN JAPAN

After the war, the Japanese economy gained momentum, and Japan's national wealth grew enormously.

I can't keep count of all this money!

On the other hand, the Koreans greatly suffered from the exploitation of the Japanese.

Meanwhile, the Great Depression hit the world in the 1930s.

During this period, after the army gained control of the government, Japan became engulfed by militarism.

A strong military must rise for the sake of national security and expansion!

Bang

The Japanese commenced a war to invade the Chinese mainland.

And, eventually, they started a war against the United States and its allies.

The Japanese lost the war after the Americans dropped the atomic bomb on Japan.

It seemed at the time that the Japanese would never recover.

It's the end for Japan...

But the Korean War (1950-1953) prompted the revival of Japan.

Boom!

Korean peninsula

In the 1990s, the Japanese were on the heels of the Americans, aiming to become the strongest economic power in the world.

Now they're the second largest economic power in the world.

But, we're going through a never-ending recession...

Just like the Germans, the Japanese

French economy
+
German economy

Japanese economy

built their national strength for nearly 150 years, establishing a firm foundation.

National strength

Thus, the Japanese situation was totally different from the Korean situation.

KOREA

Let's take a closer look at these differences.

Towards the end of the Joseon period, the Korean people led very difficult lives.

The 500-year dynasty was coming to an end.

In 1910, Joseon was eventually annexed by Japan, thereby becoming a Japanese colony.

The Korean people were thoroughly exploited.

After its liberation from Japan in 1945, Korea was penniless.

To make matters worse, the Korean War soon broke out in 1950.

Whatever was left of the country was completely destroyed.

When a ceasefire brought the war to an end in 1953, South Korea was one of the poorest countries in the world.

Korea's per capita GNI at the time was a measly US$67!

The streets were filled with beggars and people looking for any kind of work.

A dark cloud of despair hovered over the country. Hope was nowhere to be found.

The Koreans, however, did not give up. They buckled up

I'm not giving up here!

and worked hard and saved up their hard-earned money.

Start work under the stars...

Return home under the stars!

For a better tomorrow, the Koreans worked at a blistering pace to get the economy going.

The Korean economy started its spectacular economic growth in the 1960s.

Korean economy

Vroom

Using the justification 'dictatorship for the sake of development,' the military government put democracy on hold

Shut your mouths and do as you're told!

We need to put food on the table first!

and pushed forward with the implementation of aggressive economic development policies.

You can do it!

If it doesn't work, make it work!

The Five Year Economic Development Plan

The Koreans worked hard... so hard, in an effort to break free from the chains of poverty.

Looking for the good life

By 1969, South Korea caught up with the North Korean economy.

South Korean economy

North Korean economy

1969

And in 1977, South Korea's per capita GNI reached US$1,000.

US$1,000

US$67

US$1,000

1953

1977

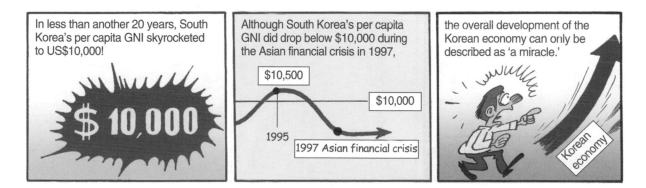

In less than another 20 years, South Korea's per capita GNI skyrocketed to US$10,000!

$ 10,000

Although South Korea's per capita GNI did drop below $10,000 during the Asian financial crisis in 1997,

$10,500

$10,000

1995

1997 Asian financial crisis

the overall development of the Korean economy can only be described as 'a miracle.'

Korean economy

Korea's per capita GNI	GNP
$100 (1963)	US$2 billion (1961)
$200 (1969)	US$5 billion (1968)
$500 (1974)	US$10 billion (1972)
$1,000 (1977)	US$50 billion (1978)
$2,000 (1983)	US$100 billion (1986)
$5,000 (1989)	US$200 billion (1989)
$10,000 (1995)	US$500 billion (1996)
$9,500 (2001)	US$500 billion (2001)

That's incredible!

That has to be a record... a per capita GNI of US$67 in 1953 and US$10,000 in 1995.

He shoots, he scores! Goal!

High income nation

Korea's per capita GNI grew 200-fold in the span of only 40 years.

Until Korea...

the highest record for per capita GNI growth was 100-fold in 40 years.

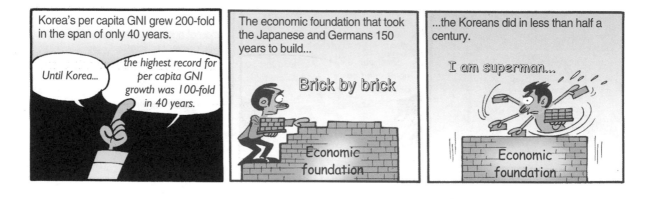

The economic foundation that took the Japanese and Germans 150 years to build...

Brick by brick

Economic foundation

...the Koreans did in less than half a century.

I am superman...

Economic foundation

It's no exaggeration to say Korea's the only country in the world

Faster! Faster!

that developed so rapidly in so short a time.

The Guinness Book of Records

Today, China, with its 1.3 billion population, is developing at a rapid pace.

* Chinese economy

But in the 20th century, the title of 'miracle economy' has to go to the Koreans!

20C

The driving force behind this miracle

was the extreme, drastic, tenacious and unyielding spirit of the Koreans.

If we say we're going to do it, we will do it!

Will not quit till we see the end!

Meanwhile, the Koreans are the most passionate people in the world when it comes to education.

EDUCATION
教育

Scholarship has always been held in high esteem.

Confucius said...
Mencius said...

Those desiring to become part of the ruling class were required to pass a state exam known as the *gwageo*.

과거*

* *Gwageo*

Whether one was able to pass this exam determined the level of his success in life.

However, not anyone was eligible to take this exam.

Not welcome!

Exam Hall

Joseon society was characterized by a strict caste system in the following order:

merchants

士
scholars

農
farmers

商

工
artisans

The upper class, also known as the *yangban*, was divided into civilian (the *munban*) and military officials (the *muban*).

兩班
양반　Yangban

문반　무반
文班　武班
Munban　Muban

Although the sons of the *yangban* were eligible to take the *gwageo*,

the sons of commoners could only sit for state exams for technical and professional positions.

This is the only way for a commoner to succeed in life!

| Doctor | Pharma cist |
| Inter- preter | Others |

Government positions and the accompanying wealth and privileges were only reserved for the *yangban*.

Commoners and, in most instances, illegitimate sons of the *yangban* were restricted from sitting for the *gwageo*.

Illegitimate Children

Exam Hall →

Commoners — prohibited entrance!

Thus, the *gwageo* was the gateway to success for only the privileged class.

Road to success

YANGBAN ONLY　Gwa　Geo

But this changed with the fall of Joseon and the commencement of the Japanese occupation.

JOSEON

The class structure that had put the privileged *yangban* at the top crumbled to pieces.

Yang

ban

The social hierarchy collapsed and suddenly... everybody woke up as equals.

I'm a yangban!

Stuff it! You sold out the country!!

The Koreans suffering under Japanese oppression did hold token government posts.

City Hall Clerk

Token posts as they may have been, the Koreans could never break free from the notion that entering government service meant the good life... success.

Hot news flash!

And the breakdown of the class system meant that anybody had a chance to succeed.

Samdori got a job at City Hall!

You mean the son of farmhand Gaettong?

Only those people with higher levels of education could hold these government jobs.

We may be dirt poor, but we need to educate our kids at all costs.

Education was the only way to succeed – this education fever swept through the country.

In the old days, only the yangban could dream of becoming high government officials.

But now, only the educated will make it!

Poor farmers sold their cows and farms to put their kids through school.

Get your butt to school. That's your only chance!

Without regard to one's social status, there was now a chance to succeed in the new meritocratic society.

Everybody starts at ground zero!

Education was the only way out... the only way to make it in the world and bring honor to the family.

To learn is to live!

EDUCATION

This sentiment still runs hot in the blood of the Koreans. That's why the Koreans are one of the most passionate people when it comes to their children's education.

Education!

Education!

Education!

Going back in time... when Korea was liberated from Japan in 1945...	there were very few college students.	If a student from a small village got accepted into college,
Korea / Japan	*It's a college student!* / *I can't dare look!*	*Old Kim's grandson got admitted into college!*

the whole village would celebrate the occasion...	As the Korean economy started to grow after the departure of the Japanese,	there arose a great need for qualified personnel. The number of students at universities greatly increased.
Go out and get the chickens and pigs! / *We got us a future president here!* / *O' happy day! Party time!*	*A new fatherland.*	University / University / University

In no time, nearly everyone was headed to college. The number of college students explosively increased.	Soon, a college degree was not enough anymore to get a good job.	The doors would now open only to graduates of top universities.
Number of university students	University Diploma / Job Guarantee	*I graduated from M University.* / *Uh huh... We'll let you know.* / *We'd hire S Univ. graduates, if we can help it.*

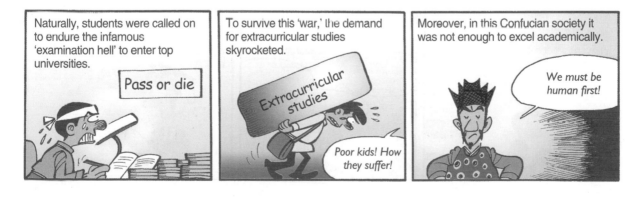

Naturally, students were called on to endure the infamous 'examination hell' to enter top universities.	To survive this 'war,' the demand for extracurricular studies skyrocketed.	Moreover, in this Confucian society it was not enough to excel academically.
Pass or die	Extracurricular studies / *Poor kids! How they suffer!*	*We must be human first!*

There was also the need to refine one's culture and character.

Education

Culture

Character

Thus, students also study such subjects as art and music to refine their 'culture' and 'character.'

Art school

Piano lessons

Arithmetic class

Chinese calligraphy class

If that's not enough, they learn Taekwondo and Judo to become all around students.

yah

Korea is full of private institutions or *hagwon* that teach these extracurricular subjects.

You'd be hard pressed to find an elementary school student that doesn't study with a tutor or go to one of these after-school institutions.

I'm having a birthday party and...

Sorry, can't make it. I have to go to hagwon.

Just call the ROK (Republic of Korea)... ROT (Republic of Tutors).

ROT KOREA

KOREA

Public schools supported by the government

Public schools

Tax

and private schools supported by tuitions paid by students are collectively referred to as

Private school

Tuition

the 'public education' system, i.e., the elementary, middle and high school and universities constituting the basic educational system of a nation.

Public education

'Private education' refers to the additional education (tutors and hakwon) procured by parents for their children.

Hagwon

Now, the people of most countries harbor some complaints about their educational system.

We have big problems in our education system!

The same here!

We do, too!

A   B   C

Public education exists to enable students to become productive members of society after completing their basic education.

Elementary school

Middle/high school

University

Commencement

116

The Korean unions are also known around the world for being extreme and drastic.

No way!

yeah! yeah! yeah!

Compromise and concession? Those are words that hardly exist in their vocabulary.

Topple, pulverize and destroy!

Some foreign companies have left Korea because of these unions.

How's anyone supposed to do business with these unions?!

Once a labor dispute arises, there are typically union members who shave their heads.

FIGHT TO THE DEATH

Vic tory

They tie red bandanas around their heads and raise steel pipes and wooden clubs.

crack

thump

They wage an intense fight resembling warfare, throwing Molotov cocktails and rocks at the riot police.

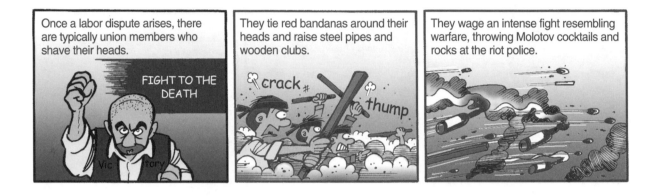

We've also seen the extreme and radical nature of student demonstrations.

Down with this corrupt foundation!

Resign, you spineless chancellor!

When there arises a particular social issue or some complaint against a school policy, the students hit the streets.

Sights of students, for example, locking down the administrative building and the university president's office

Hurrah

Time for corrupt foundations to go!

Hurrah

We've taken over!

are not uncommon in Korea.

Why can't Koreans negotiate?

woo hoo

Instead of looking for a compromise through calm and composed discussions, why do the Koreans commonly resort to such extreme means?

Where did this extreme and drastic nature come from?

The Making of the Korean Personality

Thus, there was no need for Japan to fear foreign invasions throughout its history.

Foreign invasion?

Not losing sleep over it.

Wars waged in Japan were essentially power struggles among those in the ruling class.

Who's going to be the top dog in Japan?

What about the Korean peninsula?

Throughout its history, Korea was invaded more than 3,000 times!

3,000

Ever since the formation of Gojoseon, Korea's first nation state, the Korean peninsula suffered from invasions by its northern neighbors.

Gojoseon

In addition to incessant invasions by various Chinese empires,

Do whatever it takes to put those Koreans in place!

Korea was plagued by invasions by the Japanese, pirates, the French, the British and even the Americans and many more.

Mongolia

Manchurians and others

China

Japan

United States

France

England

Japanese pirates

Korean history can be summed up as a struggle to survive from foreign aggressors.

The Korean people 'miraculously' preserved their independence

stick it

by not succumbing to even the huge empires that had conquered the Chinese mainland.

yippee~

Sharp survival instincts... pride... an unyielding spirit... all these qualities came to characterize the Korean people.

I'll die before giving up my independence and autonomy!

Now, as mentioned earlier, Japan did go through its fair share of wars...

Bang Pow

But these were purely domestic power struggles... which were inherently different from wars with foreign aggressors.

Hence, wars between the ruling class were just that, a struggle to gain power.

I'm number one in this town!

The ruling class may have went at it with each other,

arrgg *arrgg*

but it was rare for them to hurt the people

who were a source of tax revenue and loyalty.

Don't touch the people, the land and the crops.

They're all mine.

Naturally, the people could maintain some distance from the ongoing wars.

They're at it again.

In comparison, foreign invasions are by nature different.

Foreign invasions always entail plundering, arson and massacres.

Kill them all!

Take everything they have!

Burn what we can't take with us!

The people end up suffering the most, while the national wealth is drained.

In this light, evidently, a war on the Korean peninsula was not waged among the ruling class

Another foreign invasion? Oh, my god!

but against the people themselves.

Another foreign invasion? Start digging our graves. We're all dead!

Having suffered from endless foreign invasions,

Waaah!

what would have been the first priority for the ruling class in Korea?

OH, NO! yikes!

It should have been the protection of the lives and property of the people,

M-m-me the bodyguard!

but, in the face of insurmountable force,

You-have-got-to-be-kidding!

the first priority turned out to be the preservation of the royal family and the state itself.

Need to stop the country from falling!

That's how we'll stay in power!

ROYAL STATE FAMILY

Thus, the preservation of political power and the government took precedence over the people.

Shouldn't the government protect the people first?

Uhhh... No... If this government falls, my neck is the first to go!

ROYAL FAMILY STATE

After putting up a fight for as long as they could, if they felt they could resist no more, the royal family and all the subjects of the court would seek refuge at a safe place.

In other words, the ruling class would turn their backs on the people,

Your majesty, where art thou going without thy people?

thereby forsaking a sacred duty owed to them.

Goodbye, people!

There was a time in Korean history when the Koreans would successfully defeat and turn away even world class powers.

Kogu-ryo

We'll never surrender to these foreign mongrels!

But when the Mongolians, the rulers of the world in their times, rolled into town,

Russia
Europe
Arabia
India
China
Manchuria

being no match for the Mongolians, the royal family at that time fled to Ganghwado, an island off the western seaboard.

We're no match!

Gang hwado

The royal family and imperial court fled and sought refuge while the people lost everything to the foreign invaders.

During the Joseon period, the unified China became too strong for Joseon to handle by itself.

CHINA

In order to preserve its security, Joseon submitted to the will of China.

If not,

the invasions will continue.

Ming

Later on, despite the waning of the strength of the Ming Dynasty and the rise of the Manchus,

清

Joseon neverthess insisted on maintaining its pro-Ming policy and refused to accommodate the Manchus.

Choong!

What is right cannot be changed!

Ming

The Manchus then invaded Joseon on two occasions.

Manchu Invasion (Jungmyo Horan) 1627

Second Manchu Invasion (Byeongja Horan) 1636

The Joseon royal family fled to Ganghwado and then Namhansansung.

HELP!

Gang-hwado

Namhan sansung

Joseon also suffered the same fate against the Japanese.

Korea looks mighty tasty...

The Joseon court paid little attention to foreign affairs, as it was preoccupied with domestic power struggles.

Finally, in 1592, the Japanese invaded Joseon.

The Joseon government hightailed to the northern city of *Shineuiju.*

Shineuiju

Pyongyang

Hanyang*

With the ruling class gone, the people were left to deal with the ensuing disaster by themselves.

* Seoul's old name

Now, how would the Korean people have looked upon

Govern-ment

Sorry, but maintaining political power's more important!

the ruling class that had turned its back on them?

Never trust those bastards again!

They're always fighting amongst themselves...

and when foreigners invade, they run like crazy for cover!

They talk a good talk saying the will of the people is the will of the heavens...

But when it comes right down to it, party interest and self-interest come before anything else!

We'd be downright stupid to entrust those fools with our lives and property!

I'll protect my life, my family and my property with my own bare hands!

People unite!

Right on! United we stand!

The people living on the Korean peninsula, having suffered from constant foreign invasions,

lost faith in their rulers.

Politicians are all filthy scoundrels!

To stay alive, they united with their neighbors, thriving on a community spirit.

Let's unite to protect our lives, our families and our property!

This mentality, which is attributable to Korea's difficult history, still prevails among the Koreans.

We're one!

United we stand, divided we fall!

In other words, the Koreans have come to possess a very tough and headstrong temperament.

Do it!

In your dreams!

Their nature is to distrust, and not be obedient to, the ruling class.

Would you please do this?

I'll think about it.

It can be traced to the community spirit that prevailed in Korean society.

When times get tough, it's best to help each other out!

We're not strangers. We're one big family!

Unlike its literal meaning, 'to receive a helping hand,' *pumasi* does not refer to the furnishing of labor in exchange for a price.

pum = labor

asi = to receive

Instead, it is the bonding with one's neighbor, albeit within a limited scope compared to *dure*.

The village as a unit constituting a community

Skeptical about and cynical towards the ruling class, the Korean people united with their neighbors to protect themselves.

We can trust nobody but ourselves!

The only way we'll survive is by sticking together!

Local chapter of Korean farmers

The formation of such communities was based on the horizontal way of thinking that became deeply embedded in the minds of the Koreans ever since the Joseon period

We're all equal

Coupled with the strong temperament of the Korean people, all of this led to the development of a spirit of defiance.

Who do you think you are, bossing me around like that?

The Korean community spirit is best exemplified by *dure* and *pumasi*,

Solidarity!

Live or die, we stick together!

based on the principle that all members of the community are equal.

Equality!

In our relationship, there's nobody above or below!

Any member deviating from this horizontal relationship...

He was just promoted to VP.

We're still a bunch of managers.

either would leave at his own accord,

I'll make everybody feel uncomfortable if I stick around...

or be pushed out by the group...

I can't stand seeing him strut around like that!

What a total snob!

Thus, a horizontal relationship between members is the premise for the existence of a community in Korean society.

A typical manifestation of this is the school standardization policy in Korea.

I may not be able to move ahead, but I sure ain't falling behind! Lowering the bar

In this 'everything's peachy when we're all equal' way of life, trouble stirs not only when one moves ahead,

but also when one falls behind.

Moving ahead or falling behind would disrupt the egalitarian relationship that is imperative in Korean society.

As extremely proud people, the Koreans are most fearful of falling behind the people closest to them, namely their neighbors and other members of their community.

Perhaps this accounts for the Korean proverbial saying, "If a neighbor buys a piece of land, I get a stomachache."

More than simply being jealousy about somebody close doing well,

it's more of a fear that they may be falling behind.

To the Koreans, 'falling behind' demonstrates to others their incompetence.

It is a loss of face to other members of the community.

This is why the Koreans guard their pride with their lives.

What do the Koreans hate the most? Words that poke and prod their pride.

Words that will discredit them.

To avoid being labeled as a cheapskate, the Koreans fight over the check.

I'll pay for this one!

No ..no... It's on me!

cashier

You'd be hard pressed to find another country in the world where people fight over the check.

Why don't you just split the tab?

It's not like we're strangers. It would be uncouth to sit there and calculate how much we each owe. Right?

nod nod

But, if one person pays for everything, wouldn't that be too much of a burden?

Ha ha ha...

One person doesn't pay all the time. Everyone in the group takes turns...

Today!

Tomorrow!

Day after tomorrow!

At the end of the day, each person ends up having spent roughly the same amount of money. If my friend buys an expensive dinner, I could make up with two inexpensive dinners and so on.

A = B

Taking turns on paying the bill saves face, and it helps strengthen the community spirit.

cheers!

But there's always that one guy that goes for the shoelaces and ties his shoes while the bill's being paid... right?

Yes, of course.

We'd assume he was going through tough times and would forgive him a couple of times... but if this, 'shoe-tying technique,' continued, we'd kick him out of the group, accusing him of being a cheapskate.

What a penny pincher!

He's gone too far!

Or we'd consider him a shameless person with thick skin who doesn't care about his reputation.

How did they know?

As you can tell, this community spirit is deeply embedded in the Korean mentality.

Me = We

Even today, the *dure* mentality is still prevalent in Korea.

Work

Society

Me

Family

Country

It's been mentioned many times before that this community spirit is a product of the Korean survival instinct.

After all, it's impossible for a person to exist alone in society,

No man is an island!

as everyone is recognized as a member of a community.

Being a member of a community inevitably means that certain parts of one's territory would have to be shared with others.

Common parts

This would entail the sharing with each other of spiritual and material 'parts' of one's territory.

The Koreans call this common denominator of the community... *jeong* or affection.

Jeong

The closer two friends are... the more common denominators they share...

Close friends | Not so close friends

The magnitude of this common denominator is the depth of their affection to each other.

Common factors = jeong (affection)

Between siblings = uae (fraternal spirit)

Between friends= ujung (friendship)

This unique Korean trait is something foreigners, even the neighboring Japanese, have a difficult time understanding.

There is a concept of 'affection' in Japan too, but...

The Japanese are not accustomed to encroaching on the territories of other persons.

Even within a community, the Japanese strictly observe the boundaries of others.

Me | A
B | C
Me
A | B

Japan | Korea

Even between the closest of friends, in Japan, as the drawing below shows, the circles would hardly ever overlap with each other.

Me | A
B | C

Meanwhile, the Korean community, which is bound together by *jeong*,

tends to be exclusionary.

No, thank you!

Keep away!

Since the community exists not to attack others but to jointly protect its members from others,

community

---

outsiders are either the objects of struggle or indifference.

Yikes! Something must be going on over there!

Forget about it! It's not our problem.

Although the community risks everything to fight for its interests,

I won't give in, even over my dead body!

Took the words right out of my mouth!

when taken too far, the community may become self-centered.

Don't build the crematory here! xx Community Activists

Where then, if everyone's a NIMBY*?

no!

* Not In My Back Yard

For example, the Korean community spirit may prompt the public to support the construction of facilities for the handicapped.

Let's help the handicapped!

Hope for the disabled!

But, the construction of such a facility within one's community may be viewed as detrimental to its interests.

Hell no!

Our real estate value will drop!

Say No to the Construction of Facilities for the Handicapped!

Due to their obsession to avoid defeat, instead of engaging in dialogue or attempting to compromise,

---

the Koreans tend to settle things by force.

This leads to endless disputes between communities,

Can't we all just get along? Let's compromise!

Community A

C

B

No way!

which disputes often reach extreme proportions, especially when personal interests are at stake.

Take it before someone else does!

Let's consider as an example the conflict between the pharmacists and the oriental medicine doctors in Korea.

The doctors' demands are unreasonable!

The pharmacists' demands are unreasonable!

Although two groups may be similar in nature, their relationship with each other may be extremely antagonistic if their interests diverge.

oo Labor Union

xx Labor Union

oo Teacher's Union

xx Teachers' Union

This is a product of the exclusionary mentality of each community.

In claiming one's share in a situation like this,

not being satisfied with this,

but demanding this will likely lead to conflict rather than compromise.

Since Korean communities exist to protect the interests of their members,

community

the more communities to which one belongs, the more protection would be available to him.

community

community

Many people join a number of communities not only for their protection but to secure a competitive advantage in society.

There are many Koreans who belong to a countless number of community groups ranging in all different sizes and natures. The more the better if one desires to expand his sphere of influence.

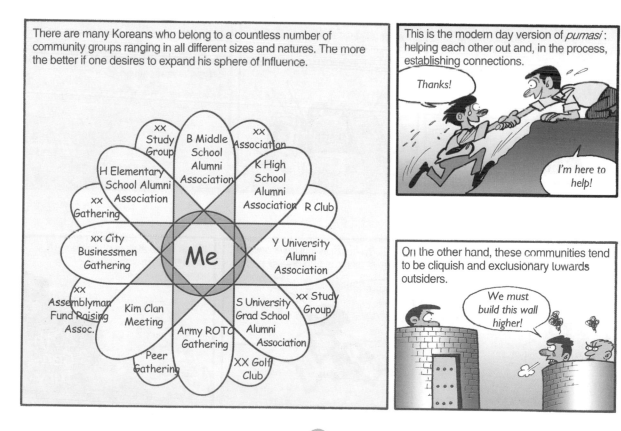

xx Study Group

B Middle School Alumni Association

xx Association

H Elementary School Alumni Association

K High School Alumni Association

xx Gathering

R Club

xx City Businessmen Gathering

Me

Y University Alumni Association

xx Assemblyman Fund Raising Assoc.

Kim Clan Meeting

S University Grad School Alumni Association

xx Study Group

Army ROTC Gathering

Peer Gathering

XX Golf Club

This is the modern day version of *pumasi*: helping each other out and, in the process, establishing connections.

Thanks!

I'm here to help!

On the other hand, these communities tend to be cliquish and exclusionary towards outsiders.

We must build this wall higher!

Panel 1:

The community mentality is exemplified by school ties...

Seonbaenim (Senior)!

So, you're also an S High grad, huh? I'll help you out whenever I can!

Panel 2:

Blood ties...

Did you say you're from the XX Choi Clan? We're related!

Oh, elder brother! It's my honor to serve you!

Panel 3:

Hometown ties...

You're from xx City, too? Glad to meet you!

So am I! Take me under your wings and guide me!

Thump.

Panel 4:

Cliquishness and cronyism are prevalent in Korean society

In this company, unless you're an S Univ. grad, they'll keep you down, brother...

Panel 5:

Regionalism is also no joke in Korea, taking the home court advantage to new heights...

Everyone appointed to senior government posts is from that one region!

That region is ruling Korea!

Panel 6:

It has been an obstacle to national harmony and progress.

Regionalism is a disease!

It must be cut out like a cancer!

This is what I`m supposed to say...

3K

Panel 7:

A strong will and skepticism and cynicism towards those in power

Politics

Mis trust

Hmph!

Panel 8:

are coupled with the exclusionary nature of the groups that exist to protect the interests of members.

Mis trust

Collectivism

Panel 9:

Interestingly, even inside the walls of these groups, there can be found a strong sense of egalitarianism and high degree of competition.

We're all equal!

Never fall behind!

community

Panel 10:

This gives rise to strong pride on the part of group members who have a difficult time accepting those who are superior to them.

This is my point... Nothing`s acceptable unless I'm the king of the hill... The greatest!

Panel 11:

Naturally, the Koreans have become the most extreme and drastic people in the world...

If I'm not to lose out to people close to me...

I gotta give it all I got!

Panel 12:

It was in the 20th century during which the extreme nature of the Koreans intensified.

20th Century

What was the 20th century like for the Koreans?

After the Japanese slapped around the Chinese in the Sino-Japanese War in 1895,

they blatantly encroached upon Joseon on the Korean peninsula.

In 1896, the Japanese murdered Queen Myeongseong of Joseon.

We'll kill anyone who gets in our way!

The 20th century wasn't the dawning of a new era filled with hope and expectations for the Koreans.

It started out in darkness and despair, under the suffocating clench of foreign domination.

In 1905, Japan stripped Joseon of its diplomatic power through a protectorate treaty. Joseon essentially became a colony of Japan.

Protectorate Treaty

Korea suffered the greatest shame in its history when the Japanese annexed Korea in 1910.

* Joseon Dynasty

Although Korea had suffered from thousands of invasions before and was located right next to almighty China,

China

there was never a time when Korea had been annexed by another country.

Sovereign nation

China

Korean peninsula

Hence, the 20th century started with Korea being deprived of its sovereignty.

Colony

Korean peninsula

It was a period during which imperialism prevailed. The stronger nations overtook the weaker nations.

Our Land

But the Japanese did something the Chinese had never done for thousands of years.

Our colony!

So to this day, it's difficult for the Koreans to stop feeling resentment towards the Japanese.

If Japan had understood the history of Korea and the temperament of the Korean people,

it would have thought twice about annexing Joseon.

PRIDE

Then, animosity between the Koreans and the Japanese would not have lingered on for this long.

We needed to annex Korea to prevent the Chinese from meddling.

This was a prime example of the limited experience of the Japanese in the international arena.

Then why didn't you annex Manchuria as well?

Why establish a puppet government. Tell me... I'm curious...

Until Korea was liberated from Japan on August 15, 1945,

8·15

the 35-year colonial period was a difficult time for the Koreans.

Colonial rule

Even before the annexation, Korea was an impoverished nation.

And things got worse, of course, with the Japanese exploitations.

When the Japanese finally left, the Koreans could not have been any poorer.

Korea had hit an all time low as the poorest country in the world.

| Then, on June, 25, 1950... | North Korea made a sudden, full-scale attack on South Korea | The Koreans fought against each other for three bloody years. |

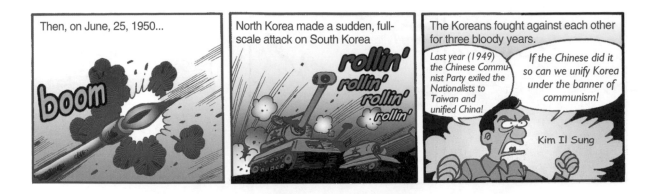

boom

rollin' rollin' rollin' rollin'

Last year (1949) the Chinese Communist Party exiled the Nationalists to Taiwan and unified China!

If the Chinese did it so can we unify Korea under the banner of communism!

Kim Il Sung

Millions of people lost their lives during the Korean War.

An armistice ending the Korean conflict was finally signed in July of 1953,

but Korea remains a divided country to this day, in fact the only such country in the world.

Caw Caw

DMZ

East Germany	West Germany	➡ Unified
North Yemen	South Yemen	➡ Unified
N. Vietnam	S. Vietnam	➡ Unified
North Korea	South Korea	➡ Divided

Even before the Korean War, the Korean people were already dirt poor...

No... No... No!

War

Water pail*

What little they had... the war took away, leaving the people with nothing but despair,

crash!

smoke and ashes.

We've got nothing left!

* A small gourd, frequently used by beggars to obtain food in the old days

---

Trembling with fear from the constant horrors of a seemingly endless war...

Free South Korea!

Unify Korea through force!

and suffering from constant hunger...

I'm hungry Waa Waa

grrrr

the Koreans nevertheless sought to prevail over their desperate situation.

I can't quit here. No. I'll start again and work my way up!

After the Korean War, the South Koreans filled their stomachs with the relief aid provided by the United States.

U.S.

The unemployed filled the streets...

Tea house

Tea room

The government was incompetent and corrupt... the stench of corruption was everywhere.

Corruption
Bribery
Special interests

Those in power committed election fraud to maintain power...

Violence, bribery, illegal acts...

Do whatever it takes to get me elected!

The people's cry for democracy were met with gunfire...

We can't take this anymore! We need a change!

Hundreds of young people lost their lives...

Redo the crooked elections!

Defend democracy!

Out with the corrupt government!

Bang! Bang!

All of this ignited the April 19 Revolution in 1960 that toppled the government.*

Liberal Party

April 19 Revolution

Finally, free and democratic elections were held, thereby giving birth to a new democratic government.

The people hoped Korea had turned the corner, becoming reborn as a true democratic nation.

The dictators are on the run...

...We'll finally enjoy freedom and democracy, yes!

Democratic Party

* President Rhee
Syngman was exiled to Hawaii.

However, the voice of the people, which had been muffled by the ousted dictatorial regime, exploded in unison...

We put you into power!

We laid down our lives for this!

Whoop Whoop

and the country continued to drift in a sea of chaos and confusion.

The people did take power away from the dictator and give it to us

I guess we'll have to comply with their demands

Whoop Whoop Government

Unfortunately, the thrill of democracy won through blood and tears was short-lived...

How am I supposed to meet all your demands at once??

Need to test the waters before jumpin' in!

as a coup d'etat was launched on May 16, 1961.

A group of soldiers led by a two-star general named Park Chung Hee seized power.

If we let this chaos continue, we'll all be reds in no time!

For a period of 18 years thereafter, the Koreans lived under a military dictatorship.

Park Chung Hee justified his dictatorship in the name of economic development.

Let's improve our lives! National reconstruction!

What happened to democracy?

Using the military and a secret police force, the Park government crushed the people's desire for democracy.

Putting food on the table is more important right now!

No time for democratic mumbo jumbo!

He desired to stay in power forever...

Park forever!

President Park Chung Hee must stay in power for life!

This is the only way to survive!

Park Chung Hee ruled South Korea for 18 years until he was assassinated by his intelligence chief on October 29, 1979.

To be fair, he is credited with having sowed the seeds for Korea's economic development.

Korean economy

He initiated the *Saemaul* movement, or the new community campaign, which instilled a 'can do' spirit in the Koreans.

The economic foundation that has enabled the Koreans today to enjoy a per capita GNI of US $10,000

GNI $10,000

was undoubtedly laid during Park Chung Hee's presidency.

Park Chung Hee's Presidency

Many Koreans today still revere and respect Park Chung Hee and his accomplishments.

His daughter should be president...

Does that bozo think he's in the Philippines or Indonesia?

tsk tsk tsk

Although history will remember him as the father of Korean economic development,

he quelled the voice of democracy by force.

Democracy...

Economic development is more important!

Economy

Nobody denies that the Park era was also a dark period during which basic human rights were suppressed.

We're busy exporting our stuff. So just shut up!

smack

He went after and crushed those people and movements that were against him

Demo-cracy

and set back the cause of democracy.

Democracy

Hypocrisy and

I'm doing the right thing, right?

Umm... Sure... Yeah... Totally!

He's so wrong it hurts...

distrust prevailed throughout society during this period.

Isn't this clown a KCIA agent?

Is he going to rat me out to the government?

The Koreans still haven't completely overcome the remnants of this period.

Hmm... Am I gonna get in trouble for saying this?

After Park's death, the Koreans had high hopes for democracy.

The dictator's dead!

Now we can become a democracy...

We've waited for 18 years!

Korea

Having said goodbye to the dictators, the Koreans believed spring had finally arrived.

Democrati-zation!

Spring 1980!

But this was a naive and fragile dream.

Dream of democracy

Events unfolded as the saying goes, "Power comes from the gun barrel."

Bang!

* Mao Zedong

On December 12, 1979, a group of army generals revolted against the existing military high command.

Rebellion!

They brutally suppressed a democratic movement in Gwangju in May 1980.

Gwangju

A former general, Chun Doo Hwan, was elected as president in an undemocratic indirect election, marking the start of the 5th Republic.. Chun was the leader of the December 12 insurgency.

The 5th Republic

The hopes for democracy were crushed again and another era of military dictatorship began.

Military dictatorship

The new government that came into existence through the gun barrel

I did it for the sake of the people and the country.

I'm not going to rule beyond my seven-year term!

was fiercely resisted by the people throughout its seven-year term.

Who asked you to make that sacrifice, huh? Who? Who? Your momma?

Seven years?? How about leaving now!!

The Chun administration lacked legitimacy...

In a country that respects traditions and orthodoxy...

this is a death sentence.

Get out

which prompted the military government to violently suppress dissenters...

Demonstrating students and workers flooded the streets of Seoul on a daily basis.

Get up! Stand up! Stand up for your rights! Out with the dictator!

Tear gas filled the air of college campuses...

Finally, on June 29, 1987 the military regime relented and announced that, starting from the next presidential election, the president

June 29 Declaration

would be elected through a democratic process, i.e., through a direct election.

The president will no longer be indirectly elected by an electoral college. The Constitution shall be amended to hold direct elections.

Korea was caught in another whirlwind of chaos after the June 29th Declaration in 1987.

The unions that had been kept down and forced into silence

hit the streets and demanded higher wages and improved working conditions.

In fact, all the factions of society that had been harboring complaints against the government exploded at once.

Because of the inter-Korean conflict, socialism was never allowed to show its face in South Korea.

But it started popping up disguised in the name of 'equality' and 'justice.'

The atmosphere resembled the time immediately following the liberation of Korea from Japan.

But all in all... despite these side effects, one act of the Korean tragedy had ended with the June 29th Declaration in 1987.

Why? Democracy found its roots and started to grow at a very rapid rate.

The Koreans now enjoy more rights and freedom than ever before...

The power of the people is now such that... dictatorships will never be allowed again,

With the great advances of the economy, the Korean people have grown confident.

Korea successfully hosted the Asian Games in 1986.

Korea: 2nd in medal count

The world came to know Korea better as a result of the 1988 Seoul Olympic Games.

We did it!

Korea: 4th in medal count

Although the 20th century started out in a tragic fashion,

yikes

the Koreans can now expect a new era full with hope and challenges.

But, due to the 100 years of immense suffering,

Coup d'etat

Colonization by Japan

Fight for liberation from foreign powers

Korean War

April 19

May 16

Ideological conflicts between left and right

Military dictatorship

Gwangju Massacre

distrust, resentment and cynicism toward the ruling class have worsened...

Huff!

Oh gracious one...

...Yes, Yes... When I'm in power

... I'll give you a position!

You guys are a joke!

Government

After having endured colonization, war, revolutions, coup d'etats and dictatorships during the 20th century,

the Koreans cannot erase the thought that they have been victims.

If I say what's on my mind, I'll only suffer...

To make matters worse, Korea's political leaders have taken advantage of the deeply rooted regionalism

Our region needs to control the government!

Good people, we have been ignored for too long! No more, I say!

Do you think we're a bunch of idiots!

This keeps people apart...

Quiet! That guy's from X Province!

Those Y Province guys always stick together!

Key government positions are held by persons hailing from the regional base of those in power.

Chief of Staff	xx Province
Chief Prosecutor	xx Province
Head of Tax Service	xx Province
Chief of Police	xx Province
Chairman of the Board of Audit	xx Province

As a result of all of this, it has been difficult to open the hearts of the Koreans.

A B C D E ...

가 나 다 라 ...

X Y Z W V ...

ㅊ ㅋ ㅌ ㅍ ㅎ ...

The Successes and
Tribulations of the Koreans

1. The Fighting Spirit and Tenacity of the Koreans

made the impossible possible
but gave rise to anachronistic competition
and rivalry in Korean society.

The Korean people tend to thoroughly finish off what they have started.

This applies to drinking,

That's enough.

One more round!

Burp!

gambling,

I told you to stop...

I've lost the farm...

extracurricular studies

Tutoring costs 10 million Won per month?

We have no choice but to go all the way!

and also work.

Let's call it a day.

I must finish this!

Once the Koreans start something, they go all the way to get it done.

Quitting half way is

worse than not starting at all!

Korean immigration to America started around the end of the Joseon period, i.e., about 100 years ago when the first Korean immigrants went to Hawaii to work in the sugarcane fields.

100 years of immigration 1902-2002

HAWAII

However, overseas immigration started in earnest only in the early 1970s, so Korea's full-scale immigration history spans only about 30 years.

Let's start all over in America!

I'm sick of being dirt poor...

Meanwhile, today, there are no less than 2.5 million Korean-Americans in America!

Go to any place in America...

There are bound to be some Koreans around!

Bulgogi

Kimchi

Naengmyeon

LA   USA   NYC

148

The Japanese started immigrating to America around the same time as the Koreans.

Let's start a better life in the new world.

HAWAII

But, there are less than 1 million Japanese-Americans living in America.

2.5 million

Less than 1 million

Population of South Korea: 46 million

Population of Japan: 130 million

Most of the Japanese have assimilated into American society, so it's difficult to find large-scale Japan towns in America.

During the Gold Rush of the 1850s, many Chinese laborers immigrated to America.

Gold!

But who'll extract it?

We'll bring the Chinese over to do it!

USA

They continued to immigrate to America to participate in the construction of the transcontinental railroad.

At the time, San Francisco was the port through which the Chinese entered America.

SAN FRANCISCO

The Chinese called San Francisco 'Gold Mountain' and built the largest Chinatown in the world there.

金山

San Francisco

San Francisco

= Gold Mountain

Thus, the millions of Chinese-Americans living in America have an immigration history of over 150 years.

1850s

In contrast, in typical fashion, the 2.5 million Korean-Americans living in America have an immigration history of only 30 years.

1970s

All the graphs the Koreans draw are this shape!

Currently, there are about 800,000 Korean-Americans living in Los Angeles.

Plaza Shopping Mall

갈비 ○○정 | 떡집 | 분식
한의사 | 안마 | 만화
머리방 | 순대족발 | 당구
해장국 | 부동산 | PC방

English need not be spoken around Olympic Blvd., the heart of Korea Town in Los Angeles.

Olympic Blvd

Hmm... Ollimpik-ga (street), L.A.-gu (district).

Many Koreans live in New York as well.

34th Street

STANFORD HOTEL

서울전자 | 아리랑 | 짐질

Empire State Building's on 32nd Street and 'Little Korea' is on 34th Street.

149

As an incentive for helping out the U.S. during the Vietnam War,

the Americans contracted Korean companies to build many of the military roads in Vietnam.

The hard-earned dollars from working under the sweltering tropical heat of Vietnam

helped jumpstart the development of the Korean economy.

When the oil crisis of the 1970s hit and the world economy shook under the burden of rising oil prices,

Oil Crisis

enormous money poured into the coffers of the Arab nations.

The Arabs wanted to construct new infrastructure facilities with this newfound wealth.

Let's build a royal palace!

Also hospitals, schools, free apartments and highways!

Offering cheaper labor, and good quality,

Hmm... I see you did a good job in Vietnam.

Price seems OK. Skill level seems OK. Credit rating seems OK.

Korean civil engineering and construction companies promised to finish projects in record time, something which was unthinkable in more advanced countries.

You can finish this in 18 months??

Yes, of course!

So the Koreans did a lot of construction business in the Middle East and earned enormous hard foreign currency,

which fueled Korea's economic growth.

The Koreans went wherever work called, whether to the Sahara Desert or to the South Pole.

I'll go even to the end of the world!

KOREA

150

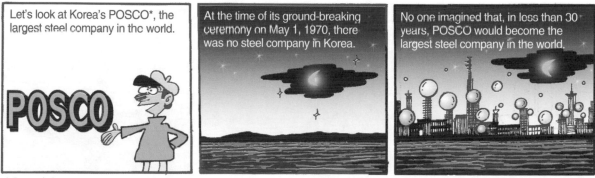

* Formerly known as Pohang Iron & Steel

However, in 1970, Korea lacked the money to fund the biggest construction project at the time!

No country out there is willing to give us a loan.

The government diverted the reparation payments made by Japan for construction costs.

Here's the reparation payment for the pain and suffering you endured as a Japanese colony.

POSCO president Park Tae Joon and all of those involved in the process vowed to be successful.

Our ancestors paid for this with their blood!

If we don't succeed, let's all jump into the Yeong-il Bay! *

* The bay on which POSCO was constructed.

In three short miraculous years, they completed the construction works,

How could they have done that within three years?

Servicing Nation through Manufacture of Steel

and at 7 : 30 a.m. on June 9, 1973, POSCO's iron furnaces started pouring out red hot liquid iron.

It was the signal of the commencement of Korea's remarkable economic development.

Nobody in the world really noticed when the Korean steel and iron industry started in earnest.

Pretty impressive!

But how good would an iron mill built in three years be?

In less than 30 years, however, POSCO emerged as the largest steel company in the world.

During such period, in addition to the steel industry,

the Korean automobile, electronics and other industries have emerged as world class industries.

MADE IN KOREA

Safe to say, these achievements were possible because of the tenacity of the Koreans.

I can do anything!

The Korean spirit of 'going all the way...' was the driving force behind Korea's economic growth.

Help!

Can't stop the Koreans!

Squeal!

152

However, this tenacious spirit

> I must achieve what I want!

often results in the disregard of formal procedures and principles.

> It doesn't matter how I achieve my goal!

> Hey! That's a foul!

Instead of opting for dialogue and compromise, the Koreans often go the extreme route.

> You die. I live.

Although Korea's per capita GNI has reached $10,000, old habits die hard.

> Quickly quickly (Bballi bballi)

> Half-baked job (Daechung daechung)

The Koreans still bear the thought patterns and habits developed during its dark past.

> Never trust anybody!

> Push ahead with all means necessary!

There is conflict at all levels of society.

> I'm not losing to you, of all people!

> I'm done if I lose... Must push ahead...

Now, competition is fundamental in any democratic society.

However, although the attaining of goals is important, it must be done in an atmosphere of fair play.

> 1st Place

But there're many times when the Koreans ignore the rules of fair play and do whatever they can to win.

Let's say a foreign buyer comes to Korea.

> Hi!

KOREA

Korean companies often engage in self-destructive price wars among themselves.

> We can't lose to Company A.

> We can't let Company B get the upper hand.

> We'll sell it to you at a unit price of $100.

> Really? Well, Company B said they'd give it to me for $90.

153

Uhh... umm... Then we'll sell it to you for $80!

Hmmm... Company A will probably lower the price to $75, right?

Ha, ha, ha. Paid $70 for a $100 product!

$30 loss!

I may not make a profit but at least I won!

What's the use of winning if you won't make a profit?

Politics is the area where communication and compromise are most lacking.

Politics is about power.

power

Power is a force that can affect not only the property but the lives of others.

In the past, the loss of power meant death.

Execute the traitor and all his family members!

But today, political power shifts according to the will of the people.

In Korea, however, a shift in political power

always brought about some form of political payback.

So, naturally, Korean politicians have fought tooth and nail to remain in office.

I'm dead if I lose my office!

Must take it away from him at all costs!

The people

Korean politics, a prime example of the tenacity of the Korean people gone wrong, must be reformed.

Another round of appointments!

Cabinet Shakeup

The competition and rivalry for which Koreans risk life and limb

Victory!

are counter-productive because such competition and rivalry are limited among Koreans.

The tutoring war!

All out war against my classmate!

I can't lose to him!

In the new global era, the Koreans should muster all their resources for use in international competition.

Instead, there's a tendency to give up on this fight and to concede that these foreign countries are beyond reach.

Korea is the weakest economic power among the OECD countries!

What can we do? Advanced countries are really ahead.

That's not gonna cut it anymore!

Korea can survive only if Koreans aim at becoming first! Look at you! Squabbling and competing with fellow citizens when you should be competing with the world!

This is no time to just compete against your fellow Koreans.

Instead, an era has dawned upon us where the competition should be against international players.

If I lose to these guys, I'm done.

We need to channel the energy that sparked the Miracle of the Han River toward the outside world, not expend it on domestic competition!

Korea is a country that produced its first automobiles by hammering out oil drums in the 1960s.

Thirty years later, Korea is now the fifth largest automaker in the world, competing against traditional automakers that have been around for nearly a century.

It's time for the Koreans to turn their unique fighting and tenacious spirit toward the outside world. A more rational way of thinking based on common sense and reason is required for this purpose.

2. The Hungry Spirit

exemplifies the spirit to strive for a better life...
and the endless greed of the individual.

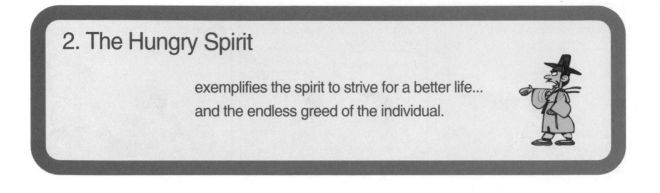

There's nothing more painful than going hungry.

Grrrrrr

The Jews teach their children:

There's nothing worse in the world than poverty.

A person in the grips of poverty ends up shouldering all the agonies of the world.

"Compared to all the pain and suffering in the world, poverty is even worse."

He died without getting proper medical care...

"There're three things which harm people: worrying, quarreling and having an empty wallet."

"The body relies on the mind, whereas the mind relies on the wallet."

Don't worry about the check. Drink up!

He's very generous!

"Money blesses a man. Poverty ruins him."*

* The Talmud

The Koreans have suffered from poverty for so long throughout their history.

This was especially true during the period from the late Joseon period when the exploitation of the people by the ruling class was rampant

until the period following the Korean War. Poverty was thought of as a curse of the heavens.

Even the King himself cannot do anything about poverty.

That's life!

Every year, the people starved until the barley harvest season.

They were forced to eat grass roots and tree bark...

When will we be able to break free from this poverty?

Hopeless, the people saw no light at the end of the tunnel.

Poverty's my fate!

Poverty-stricken people often lack the desire and will to overcome their predicament.

There's nothing we can really do about it.

But merely having a strong will won't put food on the table.

I'm going to break free from this poverty!

Without any factories in place and with throngs of unemployed people filling the streets, there wasn't much the Koreans could do.

If a country does not develop its industries and create jobs for the people,

It's up to you now!

only a few crafty people will make a decent living.

The rest will continue to be poor, without opportunities to better their lives.

The first ray of light for the poverty-stricken Koreans

shined on them when Park Chung Hee started aggressively implementing his economic development policies.

5 Year Economic Development Plan	
1st Phase	1962~1966
2nd Phase	1967~1971
3rd Phase	1972~1976
4th Phase	1977~1981
5th Phase	1982~1986

Coupled with the will and effort of the Korean people, such policies brought about remarkable economic growth.

Let's live a better life~

Korea went from being one of the poorest countries on the face of the earth to the 11th largest economic power in the world.

The people desperately wanted to escape from the pangs of hunger.

Poverty

This 'hungry spirit' arose from the Koreans' resolve to never go hungry again.

NEVER AGAIN!

HUNGRY

People around the world recognized the diligence of the Koreans.

The Koreans are the only people more diligent than the Japanese!

There's no change in that attitude despite the comfortable life in modern Korea.

Don't forget those times when we were dirt poor.

Of course, there are those who buy expensive foreign goods, and waste a lot of money on luxury items.

But most Koreans are industrious and frugal people who won't go near luxury items.

Frugality and savings!

BANK

They try to save more for a better tomorrow.

For a bigger house...

Children's education...

Household appliances...

Trips abroad...

This is exemplified by the fact that Korea has the highest rate of savings among any country in the world,

JAPAN

KOREA

UNITED STATES

Per capita savings

and the older generation's attitude toward leaving food on the plate.

You'll be cursed for leaving food on the plate. Finish it all!

The Koreans consider extravagance and lavishness as big no nos.

Have you lost your mind? How could you buy something so expensive without a second thought?

This is the 'hungry spirit' in effect... remembering the past during which they lived in miserably poor conditions.

We'll never forget those nightmarish days!

Who can blame them for that? Poverty	Nevertheless, the complexities of society demand that order and rules be imposed on economic activities. Good credit / Inte-grity / Fair-ness	As long as Korea has selected capitalism, NO! Socialism / Capitalism

its people should comply with the rules of the market and engage in fair competition. Foul! Equal opportunity	However, there are many of those who ignore the rules of the game.	Although the 'hungry spirit' has been the impetus to strive for a better life,

to some extent, it has deteriorated into a driving force for endless greed. I'm still hungry! More! More!	There are those who use every trick in the book and all means necessary to make money. Law	They abuse political connections and offer bribes for special interests. How about really helping me out this time! Don't worry! There's nothing a little political influence can't handle!

There are always those fools that look for some recognition for having made a little cash. You! Jerk off! You don't know who I am? What's the deal with this guy?	The class system of the Joseon era has supposedly disappeared, Scholar / Farmer / Artisan / Merchant	but there still exists a tendency to look down on merchants even in capitalistic Korean society. Nothing but a street trader...

'Anything's possible with money'... this love for money can be found in every corner of Korean society.

Many people worry that this amounts to pariah capitalism.

Pariah capitalism!

Pariah capitalism is a term coined by German sociologist and political economist, Max Weber.

Pariah capitalism. (Paria-kapitalismus)

It was a biting remark towards the Jews.

Money!
Money!
Money!

The word 'pariah' originated in India.

Pariah class

I'm sure you're all aware of the Indian caste system.

Caste (Class system)

Although many people have tried to tear down the caste system, it still exists in India.

Brahman	— Priests
Kshatriya	— Soldiers, Aristocrats
Vaishya	— Commoners
Shudra	— Plebeians

Now, the pariah class is so low, it does not even have an assigned place in the caste system...

*The lowest class, like the Joseon era's baekjeong**

Like the burakumin before the Meiji Restoration in Japan.

Caste

Pariah

* a butcher

Without a country of their own, living in foreign countries and suffering all kinds of scorn and contempt, the Jews in Europe were often treated as a pariah class.

Dirty jew! Get him out of here!

Without a place to call home and without any possibility to rise in social status, the beaten and battered Jews

That's right! We've been ousted from our homeland and persecuted in every imaginable way!

looked to money.

Without land or power, what can we look to for a better life? Money and wealth!

Naturally, the Jews went to all extremes to make money, which to them equaled life itself...

I need to make money!

They engaged in either commerce or money lending

Lend me some money...

My interest rates are a bit high.

and developed a bad reputation as being loan sharks...

What?? 30% interest?? This is highway robbery!

Take it or leave it buddy...

The Europeans generally despised the Jews.

You dare to receive high interest from a Christian!

May you be cursed!

But the Jews were indifferent to such scorns.

Put me down all you want! But if you really need the money, you'll be back!

Well, indifferent is not the right word. Let's say they took advantage of such scorn.

I remember this guy called me a dirty Jew.

I'll charge him higher interest!

Max Weber called this kind of behavior... Pariah Capitalism...

In other words, making money in less than graceful fashion...

Using all means necessary to make money!

What about Japan? Commerce started to flourish about 300 years ago...

Mitsui & Co.

The Japanese people traditionally respected successful businessmen and merchants...

clap clap clap clap clap

*会長

However, soaked in Confucianism, the Koreans have considered and still consider honest poverty a virtue...

Look at gold as you would look at stones!

Are you sure?

* Chairman

In this light, many people today still look at businessmen with a skeptical eye.

Hundred bucks says he exploits his workers.

Even the government doesn't trust big business and businessmen very much.

Businesses must thrive and grow for the economy.

But we must never let them out of our sight!

Why do you think there're all the red tape and the frequent government audits?

Government

We should deregulate!

REGULA-TIONS

Always only words...

Many of these businessmen have become despondent.

Whatever I do, society is going to look at me as if I'm immoral and corrupt.

In such an atmosphere, instead of looking to fulfill their societal duties and obligations,

What's the point in doing business with any sense of moral mission or purpose?

It's not like anybody will look up to me!

it is easy for them to look for only personal gains.

It's all about money! Whatever it takes...

You could say the people themselves are to blame for the continued presence of pariah capitalism.

These days, the perception of big businesses is changing.

Korea's made it this far because of the 'hungry spirit.'

Grrrrr

But the 'hungry spirit,' to some extent, has deteriorated into an insatiable desire for money.

More... More...

It's about time Korea broke free from the grips of pariah capitalism...

Ahem...

Umm... hmmm....

by complying with the rules of the market

and engaging in fair competition. It is time to strive for 'honest wealth' instead of 'honest poverty.'

A transparent form of capitalism must be established in society.

Let's stop the ideological arguments!

Korea is the world's only capitalist country still questioning its fundamental ideology!

Of course, 'the hungry spirit' of the old days need not be forsaken,

Remember the old days! Always!

HUNGRY

but, instead of fueling personal greed, it should serve as an impetus to share with the hungry and needy.

3. The Education Fever

is the phenomenon that enabled Korea to develop a remarkable pool of human resources but that also brought about an endless war of attrition with respect to education.

Building an excellent, strong and righteous nation

is a duty entrusted with the people.

Isn't it obvious that countries with a lot of talented and qualified people are going to be well off?

Naturally, the Koreans have traditionally placed a strong emphasis on education.

The government has always emphasized education

as its most important priority.

* 100-Year Plan of the State

Receiving a good education and becoming a successful member of society is not only a personal triumph.

It also brings honor and pride to the family

and contributes to national development.

Korean students studying abroad worked lowly jobs to pay for their education.

They studied through the wee hours of the night, fighting off sleep and pulling consecutive all-nighters.

They graduated and returned to Korea with the knowledge and skills learned from abroad.

During the 1970s, as Korea's economic development began in earnest, these highly educated persons made great contributions...

Furthermore, Korea's advanced education system pumped out well-trained personnel.

These locally trained personnel

and the overseas-educated personnel

joined forces to push forward with the development of the Korean economy.

During the 1970s and 1980s, education became the fundamental stepping stone to success.

It was the only way up the ladder.

Thus, the Korean parents' passion for education grew fiercer, to say the least.

As this fervor grew, so did the competition among all Koreans.

Of course, there were those like Hyundai Group founder Chung Ju Young who, for example, only received an elementary school education.

HYUNDAI

However, for most people, education was a prerequisite to success,

Although Japanese industrialist, Matsushita Konosuke, also dropped out of elementary school...

Matsushita Konosuke
1894~1989

so the competition for college entrance grew fierce.

During the 1970s, college education was reserved only for the so-called 'elite' members of society.

Hmmm... I'm thinking about going to college.

Quit dreaming! You never did well in school!

Only talented students went to college, and their college diplomas were their tickets to success.

Do you think just anyone goes to college? Even those with good grades barely make it...

College students were viewed as intellectuals.

The college students demonstrated again.

The government must've done something wrong for the educated to demonstrate like that.

But as Korean industries developed rapidly during the 1980s,

the demand for highly educated workers increased.

In response, the government nearly doubled the number of students entering colleges.

College education became available to the general public.

Hmmm... I'm thinking about going to college.

As long as you have the money for tuition, what's stopping you?

Naturally, the number of college students explosively increased,

I am a college graduate.

Now, it's more of a question of which college you graduated from...

Interview

resulting in cutthroat competition to enter top-rated universities.

Top Univs.

By the turn of the 1990s, college education became available to the general public.

Hmmm... I think I'll get a job.

You still need a college diploma!

As the number of colleges skyrocketed,

That's a university too?

Recruiting New Students

There are so many schools I've never heard of!

the gap between prestigious and nonprestigious colleges widened.

1st rate college

Rest of the pack

Whether one is a college graduate no longer matters. From which university he graduated makes all the difference.

Proud graduate of OO Univ.

Never heard about it...

Ahem!

Throughout society, the academic clique phenomenon has worsened.

That's right! Just shoot me! I didn't go to college. So what!

Academic cliques from prestigious schools have became tighter. They have become the new privileged class.

Unite!

S Univ. Alumni Assoc.

Loyalty!

K Univ. Alumni Assoc.

Not surprisingly, students must overcome extreme competition to enter the best schools.

To make this jump or not. That is the question...

Top college

Parents do whatever it takes to get their children into one of the best schools.

Run like the wind, boy!

The education fever of the parents has led to tutoring and extracurricular study wars.

과외*

* Extracurricular studies

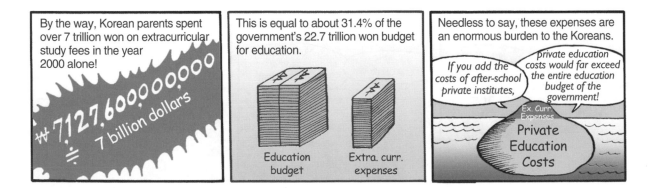

By the way, Korean parents spent over 7 trillion won on extracurricular study fees in the year 2000 alone!

₩ 7,127,600,000,000

≒ 7 billion dollars

This is equal to about 31.4% of the government's 22.7 trillion won budget for education.

Education budget

Extra. curr. expenses

Needless to say, these expenses are an enormous burden to the Koreans.

If you add the costs of after-school private institutes,

private education costs would far exceed the entire education budget of the government!

Ex. Curr. Expenses

Private Education Costs

Well, what's the big deal if parents spend 7 trillion or even 70 trillion won if it's all done for the good of their children?

The problem is that despite the huge investments,

the returns on such investments are very low, as exemplified by the low level of productivity.

Tons of money are spent,

but the system is turning out 'idiots.'

Productivity

In Japan, the level of competition to get into college is no different than in Korea.

2/3 of all Japanese middle and high school students participate in extracurricular studies.

The most competitive, top-ranked school of each country is Seoul National University and Tokyo University, respectively.

Seoul National Univ. (SNU)

Tokyo Univ.

Each of these two schools are influential enough to impact the high school education system in each country.

SNU's entrance exam will test the student's thinking faculties...

Tokyo U's entrance exam will focus on testing logic...

Korea

Japan

The graduates of these two schools are considered as the 'elite' members of their respective societies.

Influential in journalism and cultural circles.

Major political leaders...

Majority of congressmen

SNU

Majority of the heads of big businesses...

They lead their countries in all facets of society.

Most of prime ministers...

Majority of congressmen...

Majority of high-ranking public officials..

Majority of the heads of big businesses...

Tokyo U.

However, why is big time Japanese journalist Tachibana Takashi vigorously attacking Tokyo University?

Have Tokyo University Students Become Idiots? — By Tachibana Takashi 2001

* SNU's logo

The level of students attending the most prestigious university in Japan, Tokyo U, has dropped to pitiful standards.

We have kids going to medical school without learning any biology in high school, others studying engineering without knowing Newton's Laws!

Having reduced the number of subjects tested in entrance exams to ease the burden of students is creating arrogant, narrowly focused students.

I'm only interested in my major!

Major

Tunnel vision!

Tokyo U, which prides itself on being the best in Japan, is not even considered as one of the top 10 universities in the world.

Our Goal

Making it into the top ten!

And a survey run by the Asahi Newspaper revealed that Tokyo U students fall behind even students of other domestic universities.

Ranking of Top Japanese Universities 2000

Tokyo U
- Creativity: 27th
- Organization and Adaptation skills: 30th
- Professional Knowledge: 4th

What's the reason? It's the high school educational system that focuses exclusively on the college entrance exam

Pass! Pass!

My only goal is to get into Tokyo U!

and those riding on the elite 'Tokyo U' brand who have neglected to enhance their competitiveness.

Some Tokyo U grads have absolutely zero skills and a whole lot of arrogance!

Even worse than its Japanese counterpart, SNU is not even considered as one of the top 50 universities in the world.

50th

There are those students having received perfect entrance exam scores who have failed. Many others are below average students.

How can such an 'A' student flunk?

'Cause throughout high school I memorized only what the tutors told me to.

Sigh.

This is nothing but the tragic result of the exam-oriented educational system and the extracurricular study wars.

Can't call that an education.

Look at you! You're just a test-taking machine!

Gag

We're all aware that new rounds of trade talks have started.

WTO
World Trade Organization

Globalization is proceeding at a much faster pace than predicted.

Asia

Europe

America

Africa

Oceania

Although only goods and money have been able to move across boundaries so far,

Goods

Money

in the near future, workers and services will be able to do so as well.

Workers Education Medical care

In no time, we'll see American lawyers, French doctors and English accountants working in Seoul.

Jean Pierre
Plastic Surgeon

Law Offices
of James Clarke

In agricultural societies, knowledge or secrets of the trade are passed on to younger generations through an apprentice system.

I sense the coming of the first winter frost. Best you start preparing for winter.

In industrial societies, knowledge is gained through endless and rigorous study.

Devoted my life to physics...

This study leads to important discoveries and inventions.

Discovery of quantum physics!

Nobel Prize

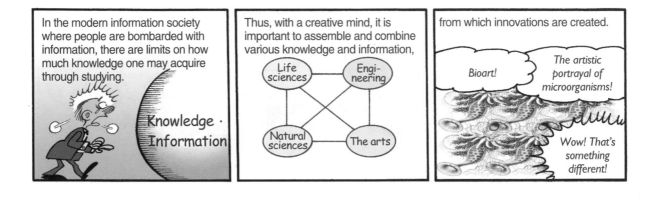

In the modern information society where people are bombarded with information, there are limits on how much knowledge one may acquire through studying.

Knowledge · Information

Thus, with a creative mind, it is important to assemble and combine various knowledge and information,

Life sciences — Engineering — Natural sciences — The arts

from which innovations are created.

Bioart!

The artistic portrayal of microorganisms!

Wow! That's something different!

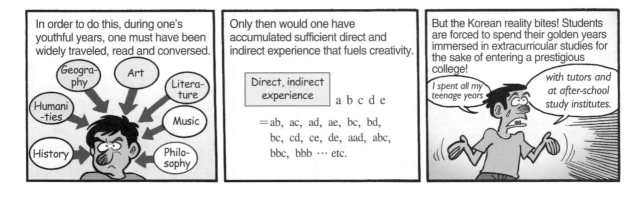

In order to do this, during one's youthful years, one must have been widely traveled, read and conversed.

Geography · Art · Literature · Humanities · Music · History · Philosophy

Only then would one have accumulated sufficient direct and indirect experience that fuels creativity.

Direct, indirect experience   a b c d e

= ab, ac, ad, ae, bc, bd, bc, cd, ce, de, aad, abc, bbc, bbb ··· etc.

But the Korean reality bites! Students are forced to spend their golden years immersed in extracurricular studies for the sake of entering a prestigious college!

I spent all my teenage years

with tutors and at after-school study institutes.

When thinking of the future of Korea, this is a tragedy of epic proportions.

History · Geography · Philosophy · Liberal arts · Music · Literature

Entrance exam

Putting all this aside, there would be a glimmer of hope if Korean students studied hard once entering college.

But whether it's in Japan or Korea, college students are infamous for not studying...

Got a blind date!

Let's grab a drink!

I've got a date!

During middle and high school, the students are chained down by their extra-curricular studies when instead they should be building their dreams and cultivating their ambitions.

Extra-curricular studies

By the time they enter college, the time they should be really studying, they go completely wild.

Freedom!

It's also a mystery to see parents end their involvement in their children's education once the college entrance exams are over.

Now it's up to him.

I've done my job as a parent.

Put simply, the Korean education fever is a misguided arrow.

The extracurricular studies in which parents invest enormous sums of money

Extracurricular studies

is responsible for reducing the competitiveness of the Korean public education system and its students.

HELP!

Students, who learn school curricula in advance from tutors,

If lesson 5 is being taught at school,

students would be learning lesson 10 from tutors.

This is the most serious problem of the secondary educational system of Korea!

naturally don't pay attention in class.

Today we're going to study lesson 7.

Been there, done that, with the tutor!

Thus, disorder prevails in the classroom.

Bustle rustle

ZZZZZ

Classrooms are a circus.

Due to such a phenomenon,

The students don't pay attention in class because they've already learned everything from tutors!

That's because what's taught at school doesn't deserve their attention.

School

Parent

there is widespread dissatisfaction with the educational environment,

The Korean education system has collapsed. We can't depend on it anymore!

Whose fault is that? Come on! Who's the one sending their kids to tutors to learn subjects before they are taught at school?

which has led to an exodus of students who leave to study abroad.

America, Canada, Australia...

KOREA

At last, I'm free from examination hell!

So, after all, Korean parents are giving away their hard-earned money to more advanced countries.

They spend money abroad in countries like America, Australia and Canada,

WELCOME!

by sending their children to intensive foreign language programs during school vacations

W....EL...COME!

Language Program

and to foreign universities even after the students have graduated from top universities in Korea.

Studying in America.

KOREA

USA

Frequently, there are talented students who do not return to Korea after the completion of their studies.

I'm going to get my green card and live here!

USA

What's the final tally? Korea ends up spending huge amounts of money putting students through foreign schools but losing them anyway.

Hey! I made all kinds of sacrifices for you but what do I get in return?

The Korean education fever, which is known as being the hottest in the world,

Education fever

Ouch! That's hot!

should be rechanneled in a way that suits the changing times and society.

Slightly cooking it over a low fire produces the best taste!

The relentless pursuit of the anachronistic goal to enter prestigious universities at all costs

Yeke!

Entrance exams

has paradoxically resulted in enormous money and efforts being invested by parents to only cause the deterioration of the competitiveness of their children.

It's ruined!

To be fair, the education fever has greatly contributed to the development of Korea,

Education fever

but it is now casting a dark cloud over Korea's future.

For the first time in history, only 87% of admitted students decided to attend Seoul Nat'l Univ. in 2002!

This may be a sign of the changing times!

Not going to SNU!

4. Bread and Democracy : The Question of Leadership

There has been a strong dictatorship for the sake of development, but a lack of spiritual leadership.

It's a blessing for the people of a nation to have a great leader.

The importance of the role of the leader of a nation cannot be overstated.

We were able to avoid troubled waters because of the captain!

Depending on the performance of the leader, a nation can either progress or flounder.

Only a capable person with vision and exceptional leadership can guide the people of a nation.

Our country needs to go in this direction!

If the people respect and believe in him,

We can trust him.

He's a true leader!

the leader can formulate a national policy and move the nation in that direction with the support of the people,

Short and Long Term National Development Plans

as a result of which there may occur remarkable development.

On the contrary, let's say some grifter, a guileful professional politician leads the country.

You really don't need to keep those promises you made with the people.

They might get ticked off but they'll forget. They always do...

What happens in those countries where the people don't respect and follow their leaders?

What a total crook! Don't trust him!

He said he was going to honor the results of the primaries but he's running as an independent!

Confusion would arise, and policies would be unsuccessful.

Let's do this!

Do it yourself!

Policy

But how many leaders out there are perfect, satisfying all the conditions required of a great leader?

Scholar-ship

Character

Leadership

Integrity

Decisive-ness

Righteous-ness

Forbear-ance

Astute mind

This is especially true in Korea where the people tend to distrust their leadership.

Aren't there going to be problems if a leader lacks any one of those qualities?

It's hard to become a leader in Korea.

That being the case... many people attribute Korea's miraculous economic growth to the strong leadership of President Park Chung Hee.

Park Chung Hee

1917~1979

Park desired to rule forever in the name of national reform.

Power

Yushin (Reform)

Do not enter

He is criticized for having crushed all those people who opposed him and having greatly set back democracy in Korea.

Democracy...

However there is no doubt that, under Park's authoritarian rule,

Modernization of the mother nation!

Korea's economy grew by leaps and bounds.

Per capita GNI exceeds $1,000 in 1977.

GNP exceeds 50 billion level in 1978.

MADE IN KOREA

KOREA

His leadership basked in the sunlight of economic growth while also casting a shadow over democracy.

Economic growth

Set back in democracy

Two choices were before him: bread and democracy... He chose bread...

DEMO-CRACY

I choose bread!

True, bread may have been a mere justification strengthening Park's dictatorial regime,

DEMO-CRACY

but there are many who recognize that his strong economic development policies, backed by his dictatorial power, enabled the Koreans to break free from the chains of poverty.

The situation confronting Park Chung Hee was to create an economic foundation from nothing.

I might be way over my head here...

Nothing

The nurturing of industries became a top priority, and Park protected and supported businessmen.

We need factories to put people to work.

Corporations need to thrive to strengthen the national economy.

Special grants

Meanwhile, workers were expected to make sacrifices for the country.

I know the work's hard and unfair.

But for the good of tomorrow, I ask you to be patient!

They endured pitifully low wages, long working hours and poor working conditions...

Low wages!

The upper brass have gone mad!

We're lower than dogs!

The suffering of the workers reached extreme proportions.

How long do you expect us to be patient?

We're human beings! Pay and treat us like humans!

But the police and army thoroughly suppressed the voices of these disgruntled workers.

You were told to be patient! Why all the whining and complaining?

The commies from the North are instigating this, right?

A strong wave of resistance and defiance by the workers, students and intellectuals rose against the government.

Overthrow the dictator!

Restore democracy!

Crush the dictator that wants to stay in power forever!

arggg

gggrowl

Rep. of Korea

There wasn't a quiet day during Park's tenure.

Another demonstration.

Take that!

And that!

But Park enlisted all the great talents of the land and pushed ahead with his economic policies.

I believe in what the experts are saying...

Full steam ahead!

Against enormous opposition, he pushed forward with the construction of a national highway...

When they decided to build the Eiffel Tower in Paris...

all the so-called intellectuals were against it. Did you know that? Huh?

and nurtured various basic industries.

vroom vroom

Basic Industries

He was successful in industrializing Korea, setting the groundwork for Korea's present position as the 11th largest trading nation in the world.

Industrial Korea

People have become nostalgic of Park's strong leadership which gave rise to the foundation of Korea's remarkable economic growth.

He was a great leader!

In the meantime, of course, those who fought against his dictatorship for democracy are never to be forgotten.

Democracy

Without their contributions, democracy would not have blossomed in Korea, which would have then remained a land of complacency and suppression.

They kept the fire of democracy alive amidst the wild storm of the dictatorship.

DICTATORSHIP

Democracy

Because of all their struggles, democracy was able to eventually burn freely and brightly...

Democracy

In the end, Korea was able to pull two rabbits out of the hat: 'economic growth' and 'advances in democracy.'

Economic growth

Advances in democracy

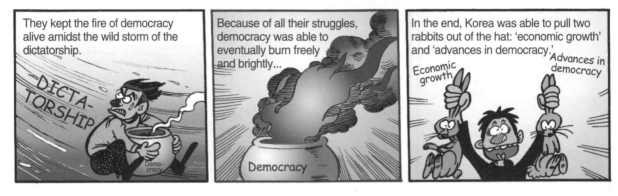

But the stronger the light, the darker is the shadow casted by such light.

Park Chung Hee

In the 21st century, Korea is witnessing disorder in its politics, which is headed by a lackluster leadership.

What is the reason for this? The hierarchical power structure of Park's era has weakened,

Power

Power structure

whereas, after long and endless struggles for democracy, the horizontal egalitarian way of thinking has grown much stronger.

Grow and be strong!

Way of thinking

Lately, the horizontal way of thinking has been prevailing against the hierarchical power structure.

Power structure

Crash

Way of thinking

Ironically, there are those who are nostalgic of the strong leadership of Park's era.

We need a strong leader like before to push things through.

Do you actually think that's possible in a democratic society?

Since the death of Park, the Korean people have yet to find a leader of his caliber.

Maybe we should just import foreign leaders.

Of course, it would be fair to also note that there are widely divergent views on Park's legacy.

He was a great leader.

He was an evil dictator who dreamed of holding on to power forever!

After Park's death, President Chun Doo Hwan's* legitimacy was questioned throughout his seven-year presidency.

He crushed democracy

and stole the presidency!

* Chun assumed power after Park's death through a coup d'etat.

Chun's successor Roh Tae Woo*, criticized as extending military rule, was also unpopular with the people.

Another military guy will be president?!

Let's rid ourselves of these ex-generals!

What did I do wrong?

* Roh was also a former general like his predecessor Chun.

The 32-year authoritarian military regimes ended when a civilian government was inaugurated in 1993. It was the first civilian government since 1961.

Civilian government

Authoritarian military rule

The people fervently supported President Kim Young Sam, who led the new civilian government. At one point, his approval rating soared to 90%!

I'm going to put this economy back on its feet!

Hurray

But this honeymoon was short-lived. The new government was plagued by scandal after scandal.

Another cabinet shuffle!

Even the president's son is involved in a scandal!

New Cabinet Members.

Towards the end of his term in 1997, Kim Young Sam was disgraced by a financial crisis which resulted in the IMF bailing out Korea.

IMF

In 1998, Kim Dae Jung succeeded in bringing about the first transition in power between civilian governments in the history of the Republic of Korea.

Military govt

Civilian govt.

Opposition party

Ruling party

Kim Young Sam Govt.

Kim Dae Jung Govt.

He overcame the financial crisis through aggressive restructuring, successfully concluded a summit with North Korea's Kim Jong Il and won the Nobel Peace Prize. He instilled hope and confidence in his people.

Kim Dae Jung attempted to restructure Korean society through bold reforms,

We are righteous!

* Reform

but many of his policies were pushed forward without adequate preparation.

Why are you just keep pushing forward without considering the consequences?

Aha! I see you're one of those crusty old liners!

179

There was endless criticism over the appointment of persons from his hometown to major government posts.

That's just too much!

We can only trust our hometown boys...

Scandal after scandal implicating high ranking public officials also shook his government as soon as it got off to a start.

Serious ethical and moral problem!

Can they act like that just because they have some political clout?

Kim Dae Jung's reputation widely varied from region to region. In other words, he failed to build a national consensus.

An overly ambitious guy who cares only about his power and reputation!

The greatest leader we've ever had!

Throughout history, the Koreans had been disappointed by their weak ruling class.

Humph!

This sentiment worsened after Korea lost its sovereignty to Japan.

What a total loser to hand our country over to the Japanese!

The cynicism and distrust of the Koreans toward their leaders have reached extreme proportions.

Everyone's in it for himself!

Nobody cares for the people!

From the perspective of the people, even a fairly capable and honest leader would hardly be adequate.

Trust me! Follow me, good people!

Does he really think we're falling for that one again?

Against such a backdrop, the leaders the Koreans did get, after the liberation from Japan, failed to live up to their expectations.

Your excellency, everything's just peachy!

They were largely clueless of the sufferings and hopes of the people,

Did you say the people are short on rice? Have them eat bread and noodles then...

Why do they insist on eating only rice?

having been surrounded by a curtain of people motivated by only self-interest.

Your excellency, you must never select this person for a cabinet post. He's got a bad reputation.

He's not part of our clique.

Naturally, the support of the people did not materialize.

Everything he does contradicts with the will of the people!

Why does he always go against the people?

Go home Ya' bum!

Most, if not all, leaders in modern Korea ended their terms amidst the cynicism and distrust of the people. They are largely remembered as failures.

Lack of support

Although the Koreans deeply distrust their leaders and are cynical towards politicians,

Pee-yew!

the flip side to this is that the Koreans yearn for a great leader,

Please send us a great leader. Is that too much to ask for?

a leader who would place justice ahead of personal ambition...

JUSTICE

IMPARTIALITY

If there was such a leader who could place the will and good of the people and the country ahead of his personal ambitions and desires,

most of his personal weaknesses would be overlooked by the Korean people,

He's got some weak points...

Yeah, but it's hard to find such a person!

who are prepared to give their undying support to such a leader.

Hurray Hurray

Good examples of this mentality would be Park Chung Hee and Kim Il Sung, both of whom are deceased.

People have heavily criticized Park Chung Hee while he was alive.

We went through all this, right?

After his death, however, although the verdict is still out on the achievements of his administration, many Koreans say they miss Park the most among all of Korea's former presidents.

Whatever people say, there wasn't a better leader.

Old school is always better!

Why? He was, as we discussed, responsible for laying the foundation for Korea's economic growth.

Another reason? Although many scandals and cases of corruption occurred during his administration,

If you stick your hand in the water, it's bound to get wet...

bustle KOREA bustle

he himself was always considered a man of integrity and principles.

I haven't heard of any secret bank account or money laundering.

Nothing's come up yet...

What about North Korea's Kim Il Sung?

He shut the eyes and mouths of the North Koreans and, by thoroughly brainwashing them, deprived them of their powers to reason.

Because of our Father, the Great Leader...

...we live in a constant state of bliss!

He was a dictator that wielded power like an emperor.

Where did that kid learn to say stuff like that?

From the day they're born, they learn to praise Kim Il Sung.

He was the very person who failed to accommodate the rapidly changing world,

Juche*

Revolutionary changes

as a result of which North Korea is now one of the poorest nations in the world.

I'd die a happy man if I could have just one bowl of white rice and soup filled with meat.

Grrrrr

The North Koreans have been totally cut off from the outside world and have been subject to brainwashing.

North Korea

* Ideology of self-reliance

They were led to believe that North Korea is a paradise and that Kim Il Sung, their Father and Great Leader, was a gift from the heavens!

All hail the Great Leader!

A hero for all ages, General Kim Il Sung!

We're happy!

What do the North Koreans think of this person who started the tragic Korean War and impoverished their nation?

Communization of South Korea.

Korean War

They, in fact, still sincerely admire and respect him.

To astonished outsiders, such a phenomenon looks absolutely pitiful.

What a total freak of nature!

Brainwashing is a scary thing!

But who would know how much the Korean people, who suffered for so long under weak and incompetent leaders,

yearn for a leader who can improve their lives?

A great leader of the people...

...but today the North is poorer than even...

Row 1:

It's tragic for a nation and its people to not have a good leader.

Good people of this country!

Trust and follow me!

The Koreans are eagerly waiting for a capable leader they can all respect...

The harder the times...

The more the people wait for a capable leader.

But good leaders are not easy to come by.

People! I'm here!

Boom

Row 2:

A person elected as a leader after having politically matured in a democratic political system with the support of the people

I promise to give the people hope!

would be able to garner their trust and respect.

We can trust him.

I agree!

Such a political leader could hardly fail.

Let's do it!

Sounds good!

Row 3:

The reality of Korean politics, however, is a far cry from this ideal situation.

So, you think you can play with the big boys now, huh?

The incumbent leader, who fears becoming a lame duck, delays the naming of his successor until the very last minute.

It's not time yet to name a successor!

When the transfer of power becomes imminent, the would-be successors scramble to secure a competitive advantage.

Hurry! Time crunch!

Row 4:

They are bound to make mistakes,

Appeal the election results!

Secret coalition!

Dirty campaign!

Crack

Unfair contest!

which lead to a vicious cycle of distrust and cynicism.

I hoped he'd be different.

Same old thing!

Impossible for a rose to grow in a gutter!

The emergence of a trustworthy leader, that is the dearest wish of the Koreans.

If the people believe in me, respect is just around the corner!

Trust

5. Learn from the Japanese and the Americans!

Korean development was based on the models of advanced countries. But it now requires an independent model of its own.

The Japanese are said to be surprised of three aspects of Korea when they first visit the country.

SEOUL

First, the wide Han River running through Seoul.

Second, the spacious Korean homes.

*Wow! 56 pyong!**

* 1 pyong = 3.3m²

And third, the wide roads.

10 lanes!?

The Koreans can't really take credit for the width of their rivers, right?

And it's difficult to compare the size of Korean homes to Japanese homes since the real estate prices are not comparable.

But how can one explain the reason for Korean roads being wider than Japanese roads?

Tokyo

Seoul

In Tokyo's case, during the peak of the bubble economy in 1989, an interesting analogy was uesd to describe Tokyo's land prices.

The price of real estate in Tokyo? More expensive than gold!

By selling all the land in Tokyo, you could buy every piece of land in America and still be left with money!

USA

Tokyo

With land prices that high, it's natural that Japanese roads are narrow!

If we want to expand the roads, we have to buy more land.

We can't pay for it!

Regardless of the fact that land prices are cheaper in Seoul than in Tokyo,

Seoul   Tokyo

it's amazing that Korean urban planners considered laying 8-lane, even 10-lane roads, 30 years ago in the 1970s.

Huh? 10-lane highways? Are you nuts??

At that time, there weren't that many automobiles. It was unimaginable that the 'my car' age would arrive.

That's wasting the national budget! What are we going to do with all those roads?

Why were 8-lane roads built when 4-lane roads would have sufficed?

Look at the empty land in Gangnam.*

If we build a four-lane road there, it's going be like a race track, I'm telling you!

* Southern part of Seoul which was developed after the northern part

It's because the urban planners who were involved in the process had studied in America.

Looking at America...

In the future, even these 10-lane roads aren't going to be enough!

Having seen the wide and spacious roads in America,

they predicted that one day Korea would also be flooded with automobiles.

When the economy grows,

Korean roads are going to get very crowded!

They designed eight and 10-lane roads over what were, at the time, empty farmlands.

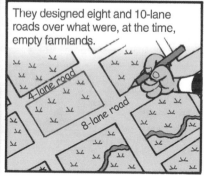

4-lane road

8-lane road

When Korea's economic development commenced in earnest, many Korean exchange students studying in America returned to Korea.

We must serve the motherland!

Korea

America

Many of them rose to prominence as policy makers in the government,

Government posts

U.S.-educated

and transplanted U.S.-style systems and methodologies to all facets of Korean society, including the economic and cultural arenas.

Let's follow the American model!

Although American standards were adopted at macro levels in the Korean economic and legal systems,

Methodology
American style
System
High ranking officials

Korean businessmen looked toward Japan for guidance.

Our situation is more similar to Japan's.

Japan was afforded the opportunity to reconstruct its economy through the Korean War that broke out in 1950.

Korean War

By 1959, Japan had fully recovered from the wounds of World War II.

We're no longer a defeated nation.

Recovery of prewar-economic standards

The Japanese government started a 'double-your-income' campaign in 1961.

Because the labor movements are becoming so fierce

we should offer them a carrot.

Income x 2 Campaign

The campaign was successful, and the Japanese economy and industries grew exponentially.

The miracle of the Japanese economy!

The 1964 Tokyo Olympic Games, the first Olympic Games ever held in Asia, helped place Japan among the advanced nations of the world.

TOKYO

The Koreans looked at the Japanese miracle with envy.

I wish I was like that.

Around the time the Japanese started the double-your-income campaign, Park Chung Hee started the first phase of his economic development plan in 1962.

1st Phase of 5-Year Economic Development Plan 1962-1966

Although U.S.-educated persons were the brains behind Park's economic policies,

USA

U.S.-educated

instead of relying on distant America for technology, materials and machinery,

USA

the Koreans turned toward its neighbor Japan from which such resources could be obtained more quickly and cheaply.

Please lend me a helping hand!

Japan and Korea normalized diplomatic relations in 1965,

after which Korean businessmen commenced their interaction with Japan in earnest.

They learned technical skills, imported machinery

and even adopted Japanese management techniques.

Artisan spirit.

Lifetime employment system

Economies of scale

The zaibatsu system, which the American military had dismantled in Japan,

Because the enemies are so strong, we need to stick together!

flourished in Korea under the name *Chaebol.**

Chaebol

Conglomerates

* Chaebol: Conglomerates

Even the life-time employment system was transplanted to Korean society.

Solidarity · Cooperation We're one family!

Quality control and personnel systems were also imported from Japan.

Seniority system

Promotion

Since labor costs were cheaper in Korea, Japanese firms utilized many Korean companies as subcontractors.

Make it according to these specifications.

Of course!

Notwithstanding negative sentiments between the people of both countries, the Korean and Japanese economies became intertwined with each other.

Japan? No way!

The economy?

YES

Since there were many similarities between Korea and Japan,

the Japanese way of doing things worked well for Korea.

Korean economy

Japanese Style

The remarkable development of the Korean economy up to the early 1990s was a product of

Korean economy

having successfully benchmarked U.S.-style policies

This is where we are heading.

and Japanese-style business and management techniques.

If that's the case, this will work the best.

Object economy

The successful adaptation of these two models

When approaching a hill, this is the way to do it.

to fit the Korean situation was the key to Korea's success.

When going downhill, do it this way!

The miracle of the Korean economy wouldn't have been possible without the American and Japanese models.

US model

Japanese model

But there were also drawbacks of having adopted the two systems side-by-side, the side effects of having an American head and a Japanese body.

Policy makers favored implementing U.S.-style policies,

Fair trade

Antitrust

Prevention of cartels

American style... American standard

whereas businessmen favored doing business the Japanese way.

Diversify businesses.

Entertain customers

Befriend bureaucrats

Make political contributions

It was not uncommon to see government bureaucrats and businessmen colliding with each other.

Why aren't you doing as you're told?

That may work in America but not here!

Inevitably, the two sides began to distrust each other,

Why do you insist on importing only from Japan?

He has no concept of the economic realities... Always spouting policies and theories.

and there has been endless conflict.

Regulation

Then in the 1990s, the world economy underwent a turbulent change.

Globalization occurred at a rapid pace with the advances in technology, transportation and telecommunications.

Goods and services moved freely around the world without regard to boundaries.

With the onset of the digital revolution,

the world underwent a fundamental change.

American capitalism stood at the forefront of the globalization of the world economy.

With advances in computer technology, the IT and BT revolutions commenced in earnest.

IT = Information Technology

BT = Biotechnology

The information, services and entertainment industries represented by the 3Ms expanded,

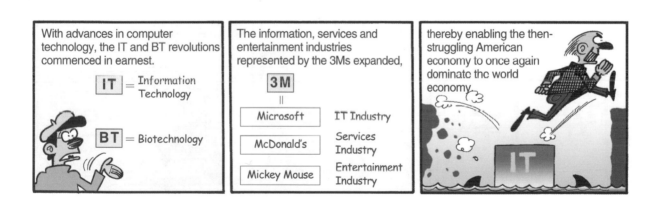

thereby enabling the then-struggling American economy to once again dominate the world economy,

On the other hand, Japan, which was setting its sight on overtaking America as the world's number one economic power,

slipped into a deep recession in the 1990s.

Even in the 21st century, the Japanese economy shows no sign of recovery.

The Japanese economic system, which was once the envy of the world,

Let's learn from the Japanese!

It's only a matter of time before Japan will be crowned world champs!

Yep!

is now struggling to restructure itself amid a totally different world economy.

Nat'l debt of 800 trillion Yen, the most in the world.

10 years of recession.

National debt

Non-performing loans

Is the Japanese economy going to be the next Titanic?

However, due to its very nature, it is impossible for Japan to undergo an abrupt reform process.

Reform

Bureaucrats

Above all, the Japanese people are slow to embrace change.

So what, if the economy's a little shaky.

What's all the fuss about?

I mean... Yes... I'm a little nervous but...

Meanwhile, the rapid emergence of China

China

is making the Japanese even more nervous.

We need strong armed forces just in case.

Korea's situation in the 1990s was no different than the Japanese situation.

In the face of a changing world economy,

European integration

Globalization

Digital revolution

U.S.-dominated world order

the Koreans remained complacent about their successes.

The miracle of the Han river!

The Koreans are coming!

The Korean era has begun!

Irresponsible bureaucrats basked in unreasonable optimism,

I'm telling you, the fundamentals of the Korean economy are sound!

Crumble

while the financial system lagged far behind global standards.

'Parachute' appointments

Kickbacks

Slush funds

Currying of favors

XX Bank

Politically motivated 'parachute' appointments further hurt the financial industry.

How can somebody with zero finance experience run a bank?

Bank President

190

Instead of focusing on technology development and quality improvement in order to boost their level of competitiveness,

businesses turned their attention to real estate speculation and irrational business expansions.

The price that Korea eventually paid for this was the financial crisis that engulfed the country in 1997.

Having been disgraced by the temporary loss of its economic sovereignty, the government regained its senses,

and instituted a fundamental restructuring of the Korean financial and industrial sectors.

However, the Korean economy is yet to fully recover.

The reason for the delay in the full recovery is often attributed to the unstable political arena and state of world affairs.

But the real reason is that Korea lacks a new economic model

to successfully cope with the revolutionary changes in the new world order.

The Japanese model, of course, worked well during the period of Korea's rapid economic development.

When the U.S. economy faltered during the 1980s, Korea increasingly relied on the Japanese model.

This all changed after Japan became mired in a recession, and especially after the financial crisis paralyzed Korea.

The Japanese lifelong employment and seniority system have created an inflexible labor market. It reduces the level of competition.

Japanese Employment System

We need to follow the American standard. The new world economy is being restructured in accordance with the American standard.

We must benchmark the American economy and business principles! The only way to survive is by accepting American capitalism!

But the American economic model was developed just for America.

American economy

The economy is no different from an organism.

Economy

The economy of a nation must be tailored after the peculiar traits of the nation and its people.

The economy

and the land are inseparable!

There can be no economy without taking into account the culture of a nation.

Can you expect German perfectionism from the Italians?

Can you expect Italian passion from the Germans?

To be fair, the Koreans have achieved much by benchmarking the Americans and the Japanese.

American way

Japanese way

But the Koreans cannot be complacent with what they have achieved so far.

Korean Model

In order to accomplish its goal to join the ranks of advanced nations in the 21st century,

Advanced countries

Korea must go head to head with world-class economies.

No holding back this time!

The Koreans have a future if, and only if, they can come out of this fight standing tall.

6. I am the king!

The desire to take the initiative, but the lack of the law-abiding spirit, characterize modern Korean society.

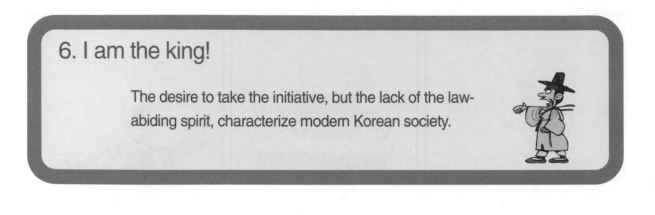

It is commonly said that the Koreans lack a cooperative spirit.

On an individual basis, each of them is smart and tough.

But, on a group basis, the Koreans are often accused of being uncooperative.

This way!

That way!

You're all wrong!

This way!

In contrast, on an individual basis, the Japanese may appear to be docile and even timid.

Hai! Hai!

But, on a group basis, the Japanese are known to act in unison under the directions of a leader.

But let's think about this. Who are the Koreans? They are a people who have survived a very difficult history without relying on others.

Having done that, why should I follow somebody else's orders?

In times of war, for example, the ruling class that was charged with the duty to protect the people was weak. The people themselves had to protect their lives and property.

Even democracy was won by the people!

With such a history and background, it is perhaps no surprise that the Koreans are a very proud and strong-willed people.

I am the king! Ha ha ha ha!

Moreover, we should take into account the egalitarian mentality of the Koreans: the Koreans just hate to lose.

Yikes! No way!

In the same light, they like to take the initiative and become the leader of the group.

It is difficult for them to submit to the will of another member of the group.

If everybody in the group wants to be the leader, the group would not be able to accomplish anything.

So whenever the Koreans form a group, a power struggle commonly ensues.

No surprise that they tend to be uncooperative with each other.

Surprisingly, there is one area where the level of cooperation is higher than anywhere else in the world.

It is the cooperation within a community based on horizontal relationships, a community with common goals and interests.

For example, if graduates of A High School and graduates of B High School clash against each other within the same community,

the prevailing camp will take all the spoils of the victory.

Naturally, a bitter winner-takes-all battle is waged between the two rival camps.

Such a phenomenon exhibits itself on a smaller scale at a personal level

and on a grander scale at a national level.

In other words, the Koreans take the lead when their interests are at stake,

giving everything they have.

When united under a common cause, the Korean people display enomous energy.

That is, when the Korean people-who hate to lose, dislike taking instructions from others and delight in taking the initiative-

cooperate with each other, such energy is indeed explosive.

The explosive economic growth during the 1960s was a result of the collective effort of the Korean people.

The government's slogan to the people at that time was:

The people strongly identified with this slogan, which helped bind them together.

The reason why the *Saemaul** Movement was so successful throughout Korea in the 1970s

* New community

was because its goal was acceptable to the people as a whole.

Although the Koreans emphasize the importance of the community,

if their interests are not at stake, even the community itself is of little concern to them.

196

This 'I am the king' disposition

motivated the people to rally under the slogan 'For a Better Life'

and it changed Korea from 'a land of despair' to 'a land of hope.'

But this disposition is often the cause of the lack of respect and consideration for others.

Bump!

This phenomenon has worsened with the advances in democratization.

How rude! He should apologize for running into me!

In fact, there are very few figures in Korea who are respected by the Koreans.

Are there any historical figures you admire and respect?

Nope.

The level of respect for senior citizens and teachers in Korea continues to deteriorate.

How rude! Not even a greeting.

Of course, the lack of respect and consideration for others

I'm the king here!

is bound to lead to disorder in society.

Law

If the people are indifferent and disrespectful to their leaders, there is bound to be difficulties in the political world.

Politicians with such constituents are likely to abuse their power,

Fine!

I'll use my power for my own good!

thereby leading to a collapse in law and order in society.

Crumble!

Another misfortune besetting the Koreans is the absence of a spiritual leader.

Who am I supposed to respect if I am the king?

There's another reason.

In other words, the absence of a father figure at the national level.

Role model

Paragon of virtue

This phenomenon is attributable to the disgrace suffered by the Koreans when Korea lost its sovereignty during its modern history. Such experience has deeply influenced the mentality of modern-day Koreans.

How could they expect to have a father figure emerge from such a shameful past?

Looking at other countries,

I truly respect you.

the Americans have George Washington,

The capital city is named after him.

Washington D.C.

Thomas Jefferson, Franklin D. Roosevelt, John F. Kennedy and many others whom they respect.

The American people continue to revere many of their former presidents.

Jefferson Memorial

Lincoln Center

JFK Airport

FDR Library

The French admire and respect Charles de Gaulle.

Charles de Gaulle

His name appears on monuments and airports.

Place Charles de Gaulle

Aéroport Charles de Gaulle

In Germany, there are Chancellors Adenauer and Erhard who are credited with rebuilding Germany from the ashes of World War II,

not to mention Chancellor Willy Brandt who laid the groundwork for the German unification. The Germans truly revere these leaders.

Ostpolitik *

* Foreign policy to improve relationships with the Soviet Union and Eastern European Bloc countries.

The Dutch revere the Prince of Orange, who led their independence movement.

Independence

They fondly refer to themselves as the Orange Kingdom.

We are the Land of the Orange...

We're not talking about the fruit!

The Netherlands

Even their football team is nicknamed after the Prince of Orange!

The Orange Army attacks!

Even though it is the portrait of their queen appearing on their legal tender,

For more than 50 years,

I've looked at this portrait.

the English truly respect historical figures who defended the country during times of difficulty.

Statue of Admiral Nelson

Admiral Nelson, Duke of Wellington, Winston Churchill...

We were once an empire that ruled the world.

So many historical figures to admire...

BRITISH HISTORY

As for the Italians,

I'm the king of the hill!

Very similar in nature to the Koreans.

there are plenty of historical figures who deserve their respect.

There are figures like King Vittorio Emmanuele II and General Giuseppe Garibaldi, who unified the Italian peninsula that had remained divided for nearly 1,500 years after the fall of the Roman Empire.

In India, the Indians think fondly of Gandhi who dedicated his life to India's independence cause.

Gandhi! Gandhi!

For the Chinese, there is a man revered not only by the 1.3 billion mainland Chinese

We admire thee!
X 1,300,000,000

China

but also the 20 million Taiwanese.

20 million of us!

And the 40 million overseas Chinese!

Taiwan

After the collapse of the Ching Dynasty, this man declared the 'Three Principles of the People' and founded the Republic of China.

Three Principles of the People

Nationalism
Civil rights
Public welfare

He is Sun Yat Sen,

1866～1925

who was also respected by Mao Zedong and Chiang Kai Shek who pursued different ideological lines and maintained antagonistic relations with him.

Sir!

Sun Yat Sen is revered by all Chinese people as their spiritual founding father.

Meanwhile, the Japanese consider the emperor as a symbol of Japanese harmony.

However, the emperor is more of a figurehead instead of an object of reverence.

The tenno bloodline has continued for 125 generations. It is symbolic of the pure blood of the Japanese people.

Then who are the great men revered by the Japanese?

The Great Men in Japanese History

They are those who built the foundations of modern Japan, which, throughout most of its history, received little attention from the rest of the would.

Have you heard of that country where the people eat raw fish?

The Meiji Restoration of 1868, which was headed by these men,

Big time reforms!

established the framework for Japan's emergence as the second largest economic power in the world.

Japanese visionary Fukuzawa Yukichi who pointed out the way the Japanese should go

Fukuzawa Yukichi

1834-1901

and Okubo Toshimichi who established the bureaucratic system of government.

Okubo Toshimichi

1830-1878

And later on Saigo Takamori, known as the last samurai of Japan.

Saigo Takamori
1827-1877

I pushed for the subjugation of Korea.

Not to forget political heavyweight Ito Hirobumi.

Ito Hirobumi

I hate Ahn Chung-gun.*

The Japanese love their heroes. They've built monuments for these historical figures and named streets after them.

大久保通り

壹万円 ¥10,000

Saigo Takamori

* Hirobumi was assassinated by Korean patriot Ahn Chung-gun.

To be fair, there are many historical figures who are revered by the Koreans.

Oh! How I revere thee...

King Sejong who promulgated the Korean alphabet and Admiral Yi Sun-shin* who commanded victorious battles against Japanese aggression.

There are also Ahn Chung-gun, Yun Bong-gil, Lee Bong-chang, Yu Kwansoon and Kim Ku, who contributed to Korea's cause for independence from Japan.

* Navy admiral who won brilliant naval battles against the Japanese during the Joseon period. He was killed in action.

Let us compare these persons to historical figures respected in other countries.

In the case of other countries, these historical figures greatly contributed to the development of their countries.

Nat'l Development Prosperity

In Korea, however, except for King Sejong who lived almost 600 years ago,

Characteristics of Figures Revered by Koreans

↓

Resistance against Japanese

Martyrs

these figures were fierce combatants who sacrificed their lives for their country.

死

Admiral Yi Sun-shin =	Killed in battle
Ahn Chung-gun =	Executed
Yun Bong-gil =	Executed
Lee Bong-chang =	Executed
Yu Kwan-soon =	Died in prison
Kim Ku =	Assassinated

* All of the above persons fought against Japanese aggression.

During its difficult modern history, the Koreans were not blessed with a great leader deserving their reverence.

There's not a single road named after a president!

No memorials either!

It is questionable whether there will emerge such a leader in this day and age when the respect for the leadership in Korea is ever decreasing.

Respect

202

A recent survey asked students if they respected their teachers.

Do you respect your teacher?

Among students surveyed from a number of countries, it was found that the level of respect for teachers was the lowest among Korean students.

Well... Not really.

In fact, such a phenomenon is widespread throughout Korean society.

You son of a... ! What a stupid remark!

All politicians are no better than dogs to him...

Nevertheless, it would be an overstatement to say that Korea would never be blessed with a respectable leader.

Waiting anxiously for a great leader!

If there was a leader such as Admiral Yi Sun-shin,

Don't inform the men of my death! Keep on fighting!

who would selflessly sacrifice himself for his country and people,

Choong!

Selfless devotion!

the Koreans would undoubtedly give their full respect and devotion to such a leader.

That's the one!

If Yi Sun-shin was reincarnated,

Let's start again, sacrificing everything we have for the good of the country!

he would be hailed as Korea's 'national father.'

But, of course, that is a farfetched dream,

Yi Sun-shin

so we would have to hope for the appearance of a modern-day Yi Sun-shin dressed in a tie and shirt.

In order for such a leader to emerge, the cynicism and distrust prevailing in Korean society must be discarded.

Hoping for a respectable leader where disrespect prevails

is no different than expecting for trees to blossom where no seeds have been sowed.

The Long and Treacherous Road to Reunification

What would be the most ardent wish of the Koreans?

Our Wish...

It would be the unification of South and North Korea...

Reunification!!

The end of the cold war brought about the unification of all divided countries in the world except, of course, Korea.

Brother!

Kid brother!

Even Germany that was forcefully divided after World War II became unified.

Absorption of East Germany

In the case of Korea, the country was also forcefully divided without regard to the will of the Korean people.

38°

Today, Korea remains as the only divided country in the world.

The reality is that no one can guess when unification will occur.

Fortune Teller

It'll happen but I don't know when...

To this date, South and North Korea have failed to sign a peace treaty.

Let's sign a pact of nonaggression.

Tell the U.S. military to leave first!

Ever since a ceasefire agreement was reached in 1953,

Ceasefire Agreement
Let's stop fighting for a while.
(But we're not done with each other!)

the two Koreas have walked a tight rope to avoid going back to war.

War

As the four powers surrounding the Korean peninsula, i.e., the U.S., Russia, China and Japan, have keen interests in Korea,

peace on the Korean peninsula has always attracted worldwide attention.

It's a matter of world peace!

Korea's a dormant volcano!

KOREA

A unified Korea would have a

Reunified Korea

oombined population of 70 million.

Germany	80 mil
England	65 mil
France	55 mil
Italy	50 mil
Japan	126 mil

The combination of South Korea's capital and technology with North Korea's natural resources and labor force

Labor + Capital + Technology

would propel the unified Korea into the ranks of major Asian powerhouses.

If Korea diverts its astronomical combined defense budget to finance other worthy causes,

Defense budget

it could emerge as one of the strongest nations in the world.

G7 + Russia, China and Korea

Top 10 Countries in the World

Unification is absolutely required in order for Korea to make a giant leap forward in the 21st century.

Unification

It is also what the Koreans dearly aspire for in their hearts.

After the unification of the Three Kingdoms by Shilla in 676, the Korean peninsula remained as a unified state for nearly 1,300 years.

| Goguryeo | Shilla | Baekje |

Unified Shilla
↓
Goryeo   } Unified
↓   states
Joseon

But half a century has already elapsed since the division of Korea in 1945.

If unification is so important and endearing to the Koreans,

Reunification!

North   South

why does it seem like such a farfetched and difficult goal to achieve at this time?

NO!

TV

Letters

Radio   Telephone

Let's examine the unification issue and see why there lies ahead such a treacherous road.

The circumstances surrounding the split of a family is complex enough.

Imagine the magnitude of the complexity of the circumstances surrounding the split of an entire nation.

The division of a nation may be classified into a number of patterns.

In the case a particular nation becomes so strong to the extent that it starts posing a threat to neighboring countries,

Everybody on your knees!

superpowers may intervene and forcefully divide such a nation. This is known as an 'external-force-driven division.'

We'll have to separate you two!

Meanwhile, in the case the people of a particular nation engage in endless conflict,

a byproduct of such conflict may be the division of the nation. This is known as an 'internal-conflict-driven division.'

I can't stand another day with you!

The victors of World War II forcefully divided Germany after the war ended with Germany's defeat.

If we leave them alone,

they're bound to start another war.

Hence, a representative case of an 'external-force-driven division' occurred in Germany.

West Germany   East Germany

In the case of Korea, the country was divided by the U.S. and the Soviet Union after World War II, without regard to the will of the Korean people.

USSR
38th Parallel
US

Thus, the division of Korea is also an 'external-force-driven division.'

USSR
North Korea
South Korea
US

To make matters worse, after the liberation from Japan, ideological battles raged throughout Korea.

The country was torn apart by different ideologies.

In the case of Korea, the country's division was the product of both internal conflict and external force.

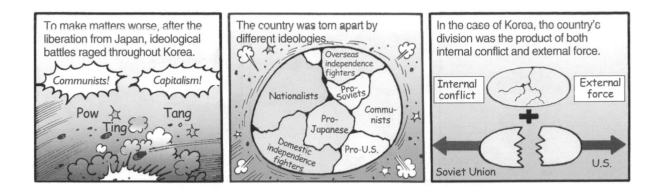

Undoubtedly, the Korean situation is much more complex than the German situation.

On top of everything else, the Korean War further complicated the Korean situation.

The end product of all of this was the drawing of a ceasefire line through Korea...

and a deep hatred and distrust between the North and South.

In contrast, despite having been forcefully divided,

there was no reason for West and East Germany to go to war with each other. Hence, there existed little, if any, enmity between West and East Germany.

In other words, the common identity of the Germans was left intact, since, when the opportune time arrived, the two Germanies would unify.

In fact, the West Germans freely traveled throughout East Germany,

while East Germans watched West German TV broadcasts. The exchange between the two sides was not severed.

Once the communist regime fell, West and East Germany could proceed to unification right away.

On the contrary, among communist countries, North Korea has adhered to the most extreme form of Stalinism,

Choong!

Stalinism

Never ever ever changing!

while South Korea adopted a strict anti-communist policy after having undergone the tragedies of the Korean War.

Choong!

Anti-Communism!

Just the thought of those commies makes me shudder!

Thus, the two Koreas have become far out of reach from each other.

Having turned our backs on each other,

we'd have to go around the world to see each other again.

The prolonged division for more than 50 years, during which even no phone calls or letters were allowed to be exchanged, caused

North and South Korea to drift apart to such an extent that they have become totally different societies.

North

South

All Hail the Great Leader, Kim Il Sung!

Spring Bargain Sale

In addition, North Korea continues insisting on realizing unification through the communization of South Korea,

Free the people of South Korea!

Socialist Unification

while, of course, South Korea continues rejecting such an idea.

Don't even think of it!

We gave up our lives for this freedom!

Freedom Democracy

Thus, the two Koreas are yet to have a meeting of the minds on even the most basic first step to unification.

vroom

put

put

Nevertheless, neither side can afford to give up on this most important goal.

We must overcome this division!

So the South insists on pursuing unification in accordance with its plan and vice versa.

North Unification Plan

South Unification Plan

Let's see how these plans differ,

Comparison of Unification Plans of South and North Korea

by first taking a look at the South Korean plan.

South Korea's Plan for Unification

With the fall of the Eastern European Bloc in 1989, the cold war was brought to an end.

Ideological conflict

It's the economy, stupid!

Accordingly, South Korea's policy on North Korea also underwent a significant change.

So far, we've considered the North Koreans to be only the objects of confrontation and hostility.

We may be divided but the 70 million Koreans living on the peninsula are all members of the same community.

The two Koreas must restore and develop the national community through open exchanges and cooperation based on the principle of co-existence and co-prosperity.

Ehh?

South Korea's new policy on North Korea was dubbed the 'Korean Community Unification Plan.'

Korean Community Unification Plan

Sept. 11, 1989

There are three principles that are conditions precedent to the implementation of this unification plan.

Autonomy

Peace

Democracy

Autonomy Since unification is a matter to be resolved by the Koreans,

This is a matter to be resolved by the Koreans only.

Unification

any decisions regarding the matter must be made by the Koreans themselves without the intervention of outside forces.

Why should outsiders be involved?

Yes! It's a matter of national pride!

Peace Having suffered unspeakable horrors during the Korean War,

Korean War

it is imperative that the two Koreas reject any attempts to resort to force and violence in the unification process,

NEVER!

so that unification may be achieved through peaceful means.

What's the use of unification if we have to spill blood again!

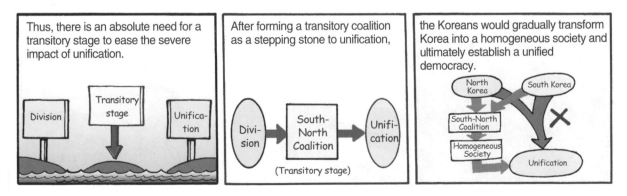

What is important here is that the South-North Coalition is not a coalition between the South and North Korean governments.

Coalition Government ✕

South Korean Government → Coalition Government ← North Korean Government

---

It is a special relationship that transcends such dimensions.

South Korean Government → South-North Coalition ← North Korean Government

---

Under this arrangement, the South and North Korean governments would, for the time being, maintain their sovereignty.

This year's national budget would be...

Increase the budget for national defense. Meet with the Americans...

South Korean Government

North Korean Government

Through the South-North Coalition, the two Koreas would start to promote economic and cultural exchanges and cooperation.

Economy Culture South-North Coalition

It would be a transitory stage during which

---

the groundwork for a unified nation would be laid.

North

South

South-North Coalition

Starting with summit meetings

South-North Summit

---

and inter-Korean ministerial meetings,

Inter-Korean Ministerial Meeting

---

which would lead to the establishment of a council consisting of representatives from South and North Korea,

South-North Council

---

the South-North Coalition would serve as the stepping stone to unification as well as its preparatory body.

Inter-Korean Ministerial Meeting

Politics
Foreign Affairs
Economy
Defense
Society Culture

Various Standing Committees

Through the South-North Coalition, the Koreans would recover homogeneity as one people

North Korea

South Korea

South-North Coalition

Restoration of national homegeneity

---

and eventually establish through peaceful means a unified government.

North Korea South Korea → Restoration of Homogeneity

National Coalition

Unified Government

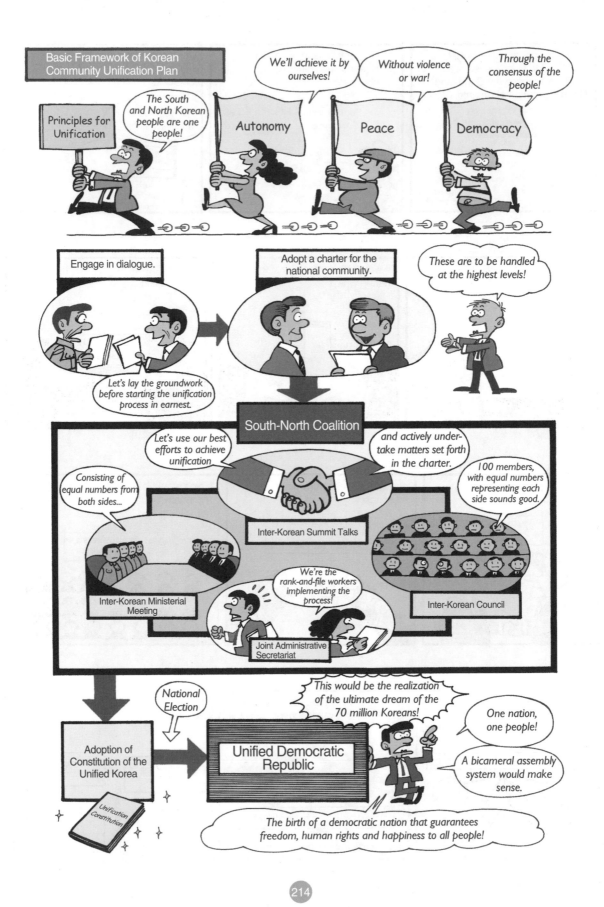

Well, that's the South Korean plan... Now, what's the Korean Federation Unification Plan proposed by North Korea?

Korean Federation

A federation is a nation consisting of two or more states.

A nation consisting of 50 states

We consisted of a number of republics.

USA

Former USSR

The United States offers a good example.

Federal Gov't (Central Gov't)

Local Gov't — Local Gov't — Local Gov't

Limited Sovereignty

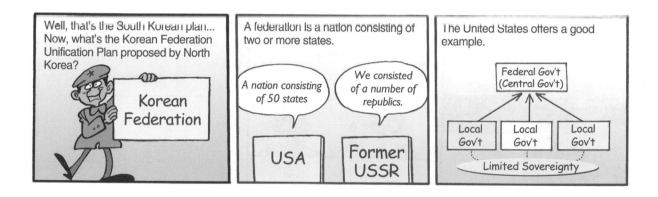

The United States has a well developed federal system of government.

50 states constitute the United States.

California State Govt.

Texas State Govt.

Virginia State Govt.

⋮

Etc, Etc., 50 States

Each state is governed by its own government. The nation as a whole, however, is governed by the federal government.

Federal Government — State

State — Washington D.C. — State

State — State

Each state government is autonomous to a certain extent, with the power to run its local affairs.

This year's budget will be...

Let's increase the education budget and start the school year earlier...

Texas

Virginia

The federal government is delegated with certain powers.

If each state had its own currency, its own army and its own interest rates,

there would arise massive disorder!

Federal Government

For example, California State and Gyeonggi Province* are free to establish trade relations with each other,

Let's exchange technologies.

Invest in our province!

California State-Gyeonggi Province Trade Agreement

* One of the provinces constituting the Republic of Korea

but the power to handle diplomatic relations at the national level is delegated to the federal government.

Peace on the Korean peninsula is very important to us.

The U.S. is behind you 100%.

The federal government is responsible for foreign affairs, national defense and national economic policy...

Foreign Affairs — Defense — Economy

Central Gov't

In a way, the federal government is superior to the 50 state governments.

Federal Government

State Government

The federal system espoused by North Korea resembles the U.S. and German federal systems.

America, Switzerland, Canada... They're all doing it!

We can do it, too!

Federal System

Under this system, South and North Korea would maintain their individual sovereign governments

Let's not interfere with each other's affairs...

Pick your teeth with a lamppost for all I care!

South Korean Govt.

North Korean Govt.

under a superior federal government,

Federal Government

↑ South Korean Govt.

↑ North Korean Govt.

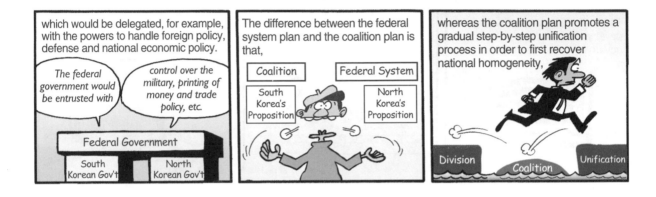

which would be delegated, for example, with the powers to handle foreign policy, defense and national economic policy.

The federal government would be entrusted with

control over the military, printing of money and trade policy, etc.

Federal Government

South Korean Gov't

North Korean Gov't

The difference between the federal system plan and the coalition plan is that,

Coalition — South Korea's Proposition

Federal System — North Korea's Proposition

whereas the coalition plan promotes a gradual step-by-step unification process in order to first recover national homogeneity,

Division | Coalition | Unification

the federal system plan first calls for the creation of a unification government,

We must unify first!

Otherwise, the process will take too long!

after which the issue of national homogeneity is to be considered.

Let's get the unification thing over... Then, worry about the rest!

Division | Unification

Sounds like a great idea at first, right?

They may have a point there.

If we wait too long, it may take forever!

What's the big deal as long as each side recognizes the sovereignty of the other? After all, wouldn't this approach expedite the unification process?

There's really no good reason to oppose the federal system!

The reason why South Korea cannot accept the federal system plan

No way!

Federal system

is because of the three preconditions insisted upon by North Korea.

Preconditions

Federal system

First condition. Withdraw the U.S. forces from South Korea.

Go Home!

Korean peninsula

U.S. FORCES

Second condition. Repeal the National Security Law.

National Security law

Third condition. Legalize the activities of the Communist Party in Korea.

You talk about unification without outside interference, but you maintain foreign military forces on the peninsula!

The U.S. is an imperialistic country just waiting to invade and take over North Korea!

US

Unification can never happen with the U.S. military on Korean soil!

US

USA

And what about the National Security Law? It punishes anyone coming into contact with, or speaking favorably of, North Korea.

North Korea

National Security Law

With this kind of law in place, how are we even supposed to discuss unification?

Only when you repeal this law, will North and South Koreans be able to meet and discuss the possibilities of a peaceful unification!

Legalize the Communist Party! How's reunification supposed to happen when the South Koreans implement such drastic anti-communist policies!

Legalize the Communist Party!

And, of course... if a free, democratic and unified Korea is born, the people must enjoy ideological freedom.

Ideological Freedom

Korean Federation

Capitalism South Korea

Communism North Korea

How would the freedom to engage in political activities be guaranteed if the Communist Party continues to be outlawed?

Thus, despite its overwhelming military might, North Korea has not been able to 'swallow' South Korea

North Korea   South Korea

Crunch!

due to the presence of the U.S. military in South Korea.

Oh, that little

If the U.S. military were to withdraw from South Korea,

this would break the balance of power on the Korean peninsula.

he he he

With only a ceasefire agreement in place,

Nobody will get in the way anymore, right!

there would be no other mechanism that would deter an invasion by North Korea.

crack

The same logic applies to North Korea's demand to repeal the National Security Law.

It's an obstacle to unification!

National Security Law

The National Security Law was enacted in order to promote national security and to restrict antigovernment activities.

Overthrow the government!

National Security Law
Law No. 3318
1980. 12. 31.

Unification through communization!

This statute replaced the previous version of the National Security Law and the Anti-Communism Law.

National Security Law
Law No. 549
1963. 6. 10.

정지 *

Anti-Communism Law
Law No. 643
1961. 7. 3.

* Repealed

The National Security Law prescribes certain organizations as anti-state organizations and strictly restricts their activities.

National Security Law

An anti-state organization refers to an organization that was formed for subversive purposes or

The incumbent government needs to hit the road!

Until then, we're in charge! We'll overthrow this government and start a new era!

to adhere to communist-related lines of activities with such purposes.

XX Democratic Youths

XX Unification Society

Workers' Revolution XX

People's Revolutionary XX

Revolutionaries of XX

The National Security Law was enacted in 1980 by the new military regime that staged a coup d'etat on December 12, 1979*.

Freeze!

bang bang

Or else!

* See page 142.

Its purpose was to preserve the security of the new regime

Ra ra

What's all the racket about??

by persecuting opposition forces as anti-state organizations.

National Security Law

Democracy!

The National Security Law enabled the government to accuse anyone of engaging in anti-state activities.

You commie sympathizer!

Many people cried out for its outright repeal.

Abolish the National Security Law!

However, to a certain extent, the National Security Law does serve as a device to preserve national security.

National Security Law

State

Its outright repeal would result in the disarmament of Korean society.

Now, I can freely go to North Korea!

Yippee! All hail the Dear Leader, Kim Jong Il!

True, there is a need to substantially amend the statute,

The voice of the conscience!

National Security Law

NO!

but its outright repeal may result in the infiltration of harmful elements from North Korea.

Let's fire up those anti-American sentiments!

Let's stomp out the American imperialists in the name of the people!

In such case, there is a great risk that South Korean society would be overwhelmed by disorder and conflict.

That's why it's impossible to accept the North Korean demands.

Scrapping the National Security Law without offering a better alternative will not do!

Nat'l Security Law

What about the condition that South Korea permit the activities of the Communist Party?

That's old school! Try this!

Legalization of Communist Party

Anti-Communism

North Korea is a strictly controlled society.

If we even listen to South Korean broadcasts...

we'll be thrown in jail!

Compared to the North Koreans who have been brainwashed to blindly accept the communist ideology,

We're very happy!

We're living in paradise!

Three cheers for our great socialist republic!

the South Koreans are accustomed to the free exchange of ideas and opinions, the bedrock principles of a democratic society.

Freedom of speech!

Equal opportunity!

Gender equality!

If communism were to be permitted in South Korea,

Go out on an all-out strike to paralyze the economy!

Will do, my comrade!

forces backed by North Korea may agitate student groups and labor unions,

among others, thereby wreaking havoc on South Korean society.

South Korea

Of course, if North Korea were to open its doors and embrace democracy,

North Korea

and guarantee basic rights,

Let's go for capitalism!

Say no to communism!

Every communist country has fallen!

North Korea

there would be no reason to oppose the Communist Party.

All kinds of political expressions can be made!

That's true democracy at work!

Guarantee of rights and freedom

North Korea's one-sided demands, however,

You guys change! We don't have anything to change!

are the product of its ulterior motives.

There's no other way to unify!

Unification through Communization

North Korea

That is, North Korea continues to insist on its federal system unification plan due to its desire to achieve unification through communization.

I told you that's not going to happen!

So far, we have looked at the proposed plans for unification of South and North Korea.

South Korean Plan

North Korean Plan

If both sides truly wish to unify the Korean peninsula,

Unification

it goes without saying that there should be room for compromise between the two sides.

We can compromise on that...

I'm sure we can work something out.

But if North Korea adamantly adheres to its position to communize South Korea,

Communization

I'd rather die than accept that!

the Korean peninsula could remain divided indefinitely.

Communist rule!

Over my dead body!

Thus, any progress can be made only if North Korea drops this position.

Continuing to insist on the communization

of South Korea is nothing more than a ploy to maintain the status quo.

In fact, it is doubtful as to whether North Korea truly believes it could realize the communization of South Korea.

That's what I've been saying but to be honest with you...

This is so because, except for its well-oiled military machine,

North Korea, especially its economy, is literally sinking.

SOS! America! South Korea! Japan!

We're starving here! Send over some rice!

North Korea

In contrast, South Korea is now ranked as the 13th largest economy in the world with a per capita GNI of US$10,000.

South Korea
$

North Korea
$

$300 $10,000

The sheer difference in the sizes of the two economies is a factor that discourages North Korea from acting on its professed goal.

You've put on some weight, I see!

yikes!

R.O.K

Of course, North Korea is also aware that South Korea would not sit by idly if there are any attempts to forcefully unify the Korean peninsula.

Communist Aggression=War= U.S. Involvement

It's a no-win game...

If this is the case, why wouldn't North Korea just drop such a drastic policy line?

We should take into account that the North Korean regime maintains a large armed forces numbering over 1 million.

As the Defense Chairman, I'm the supreme leader!

All Hail the Dear Leader!

The justification for maintaining such a large military is the 'liberation' of South Korea.

Liberation of South Korea!

Communist Unification!

If North Korea were to renounce its policy line to 'liberate' South Korea, it would be forsaking the very foundation on which its regime is built.

Renunciation of Policy Line → Renunciation of War → No Justification for Maintaining Large Armed Forces

Needless to say, powerful military leaders would vehemently oppose any such development.

If there's going to be no war, what are we doing here?

We're all gonna be jobless. I can just tell!

So, the North Korean regime would risk undergoing a collapse.

군 Military Circles 부

In other words, the survival of the North Korean regime for over 50 years

North Korean Government 1945-Present

was based on this foundation.

Until the day of unification,

...Let's follow the Great Leader and overcome all hardships!

This is why North Korea continues to profess a desire to achieve unification through communization even though the times have changed.

communization

Why don't you sing to another tune?

The times have indeed changed. The Eastern European Bloc and, in fact, most communist countries have disappeared.

crumble

Communist regimes

Europe

Germany has unified. But it was communist East Germany that was merged into West Germany.

This, of course, was a tremendous shock to North Korea.

D DDR

North Korea... the only hardline Stalinist state left in the world...

Still? Give it up guys!

Stalinism

North Korea

Even their most trusted ally, China, has turned to capitalism...

N-no!

Love the smell of money! Good luck!

Undoubtedly, this has made North Korea very uneasy.

Nobody's on our side!

The lure of money has changed the Chinese and Russians!

North Korea may be tempted to go the path of an all-out war with South Korea,

Why I oughta just roll right through South Korea!

But it does not stand a chance against the combined South Korean-U.S. forces.

USA

Those U.S. imperialists!

If a war broke out, North Korea's very foundation would be turned upside down.

South Korea, of course, would suffer...

but so would we. Maybe more!

North Korea is not foolish enough to risk losing everything like that.

Where would I sleep?

I can't stand the cold!

But the North Korean dilemma is that it is also not in a position to pursue Chinese-style reforms.

Maybe I should just open it all up...

Such reforms would remove barriers to information on the outside world

radios

news-papers

businessmen

information

books

tourists

and provoke the North Korean people who were deceived for decades about the truth of their situation.

They told us that South Koreans were all beggars!

But they have so much rice, a lot of it is just thrown away!

Thus, the opening up of North Korea and the implementation of reforms are likely to lead to the fall of the North Korean regime.

How dare you deceive the people like this!

Out with the regime that starved the people!

Against such a backdrop, it is obvious what the North Korean regime has in mind.

We really want the unification of Korea...

...b-but...

Given that the 'liberation' of South Korea is now a farfetched dream,

Bye, bye!

Communization

and that its economy is on the verge of collapse, North Korea has no alternative but to open its doors and implement reforms.

Yes, I know opening our doors is the only way but...

Come out and play!

That would lead to the collapse of the regime! We would be absorbed by South Korea!

The more they come into contact with South Korea, the more the North Koreans would realize how affluent the South Koreans are.

They say South Koreans eat rice everyday, right?

That's unimaginable for us!

Obviously, this would put the North Korean regime in a precarious position.

But I hear the women are starving.

You mean they're dieting.

We must avoid outside contact at all costs! Leave us alone!

Reunion of separated families? Prevent it from happening!

Family reunions? No way!

Summit talks? Use any excuse to avoid it!

We're canceling the summit talks. Don't ask why!

North Korea's ulterior motive is to cut off ties with South Korea in order to safeguard the stability of its regime.

Unification? Why, of course!

No way!

Nevertheless, in order to rebuild its floundering economy, North Korea badly needs cash from South Korea.

So its strategy is to squeeze as much money as it can from South Korea

but to minimize contact in order to prevent the opening of North Korea.

The idea is to take

but not to give!

At that time, West Germany was the most affluent nation in Western Europe,

whereas East Germany was the most affluent nation in Eastern Europe.

Highest per capita GNI among socialist countries

Nevertheless, there was a very large disparity between the income of West Germans and East Germans (by as much as 10-fold).

West Germany

East Germany

$30,000

$3,000

After unification, West Germany poured astronomical sums of money into the reconstruction of East Germany.

gluck
gluck

This has been going on for more than 10 years.

No end in sight!

However, there still exists a large gap between the standards of living of the West and East Germans.

Thus, it is yet unknown how much more money will be required.

When will this end?

Of course, the costs of unification come from taxpayers' money.

Unif. Costs

tax

tax

The West Germans have been patient about the tax increases, but there is some concern.

What can we do... They're Germans too...

We'd have to pay for it one way or the other...

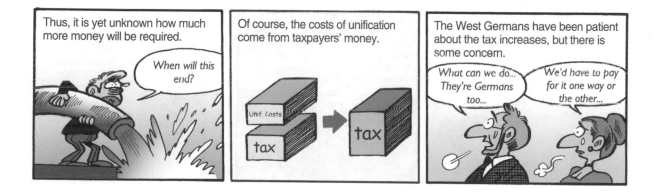

If West Germany's economy had not been strong enough

grrr

to sustain such a burden,

Unification Costs

both West and East Germany would have collapsed under the weight of the enormous costs of unification.

crash

Unification Costs

Sorry for having you shoulder everything.

What would happen if the Korean peninsula was suddenly unified? Obviousy, South Korea would have to bear the burden of unification.

Unification costs

We should consider that the disparity between the North and South Korean economies is larger than that in the case of Germany.

South Korea

North Korea

The size of such disparity is more than four times that in the case of Germany. But Korea's per capita GNI is only 1/3 ot the former West Germany.

$30,000

$10,000

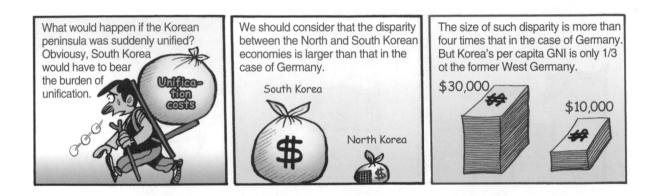

If we do some simple math, the unification costs to be borne by the Koreans on a per capita basis

West and East Germany	North and South Korea

Disparity in GNI	10 times : 40 times

➡ 4 times

West Germany's GNI	3 : 1	South Korea's GNI

is more than 12 times the unification costs borne by the Germans on a per capita basis.

South Korean Burden

West German Burden

Of course, this would be an unrealistic burden for South Korea.

This would lead to

the collapse of both Koreas!

Unification

No matter how important unification is to us,

how many of us would want to go to such extremes?

Even without considering unification, I'm breaking my back here paying for my kid's education!

What would happen if the taxes were raised manyfold?

East Germany was the most affluent communist country when it was absorbed into West Germany, whereas North Korea is now one of the poorest countries in the world.

The costs of reconstructing North Korea would be staggering–nothing like the German experience in terms of the magnitude.

Impossible!

In fact, the lesson learned from the German experience was to not approach unification in such a fashion.

You're opposing unification just because of the economics? You traitor!

You're full of it! I need to feed my family first!

Needless to say, there is also the ideological difference between the South and North Koreans.

Even though North Korea is an extremely poor country, as residents of a socialist state, its people believe that they live in an egalitarian society.

Comrade! *Comrade!* *Comrade!*

Even though they are equal only in their poverty, egalitarianism is deeply embedded in the minds of the North Koreans.

Thus, it would be difficult for them to accept the gap between the rich and the poor and their low status in unified Korean society.

If North Korea adopts capitalism after unification,

North

Capitalism

it is likely that the North Koreans would have no alternative but to work for South Korean capitalists.

Work hard or you will get the axe!

There would be discontent over the inequalities characterizing the new society.

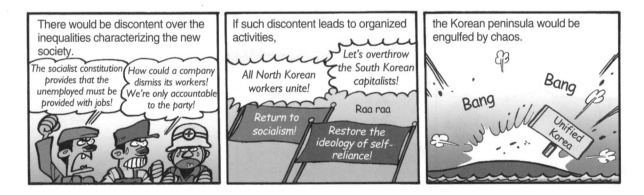

The socialist constitution provides that the unemployed must be provided with jobs!

How could a company dismiss its workers! We're only accountable to the party!

If such discontent leads to organized activities,

All North Korean workers unite!

Let's overthrow the South Korean capitalists!

Return to socialism!

Raa raa

Restore the ideology of self-reliance!

the Korean peninsula would be engulfed by chaos.

Bang

Bang

Unified Korea

Both sides worry about this possibility...

It's something we'll have to go through at some point...

Although both South and North Korea voice their desire for unification, reality dictates that each side tread cautiously as it seeks to achieve this goal.

We wish for and dream of unification~

Don't come near us! Stay away! Leave us alone!

We must tread carefully and not rush the process...

230

However, sooner or later, the two Koreas will have to deal with the problem of unification in earnest.

Unification

Out of fear that its regime may collapse, North Korea avoids any interaction with South Korea.

Leave me alone!

It is possible that North Korea may resort to extreme means to overcome its current predicament.

I could take this sitting down...

or going all the way!

For this reason, the threat of war continues to exist on the Korean peninsula.

Korean peninsula

The problem is that, although the North Korean economy is on the brink of bankruptcy,

Father, I'm hungry!

There's nothing to eat. What can I do?

North Korea continues to distrust South Korea.

You guys say you don't want to absorb North Korea.

But I think you're waiting for us to just collapse, right?

It's not in our best interest to have North Korea undergo a sudden failure!

The day we fall, you'll take over everything, right?

In this regard, South Korea has adopted an engagement policy

to bring North Korea to the negotiation table in order to gain its trust and avoid the risk of war.

If nothing else, we must avoid war!

It is a policy of tolerance and cooperation to grow together through economic and cultural exchanges.

This is the so-called Sunshine Policy.

There appears to be no other alternative today but for South Korea to pursue such an engagement policy.

Reconciliation and cooperation...

or war...

or eternal division!

However, a one-sided engagement policy

Come out... Let's talk over a nice hot meal!

will not achieve much.

Hold on a second!

He's coming!

Instead, it would only 'spoil' North Korea.

I want some steamed ribs next time!

The Sunshine Policy is modeled after the Ospolitik of former West German Chancellor Willy Brandt.

Ostpolitik

Willy Brandt

In 1970, West and East Germany signed a treaty

We're one people.

Let's end the antagonism.

West Germany

East Germany

that liberalized West German travel to East Germany.

West Germany

East Germany

In exchange, West Germany provided a significant economic aid package to East Germany.

We'll pay this much every year.

We'll give you more if you need it.

However, the West Germans did not politically take advantage of this new development.

We've worked this hard for unification!

Vote for us in the next elections!

But at the same time, West Germany did not blindly confer aid on East Germany.

If you don't agree to these terms...

.... We're not paying for that highway!

Okay.

They ensured that the benefit of economic aid was shared by the people of both West and East Germany.

West

$

East

Benefits

This is how they built the foundation for German unification.

Why can't we be like the Germans and deal with North Korea on a give-and-take basis?

It's a different case here! Unification is not a business proposition!

This, in fact, is what should be the model for the Sunshine Policy of Korea.

We need to touch their hearts first...

That'll take forever!

Sincerity moves the heavens!

Faced by crises on all sides, North Korea has become more sensitive than ever before.

Fall of communism
War against terrorism
Economic crisis
Lock 'em down!

For the time being, it would be difficult for North Korea to open up and implement reforms.

Reform = Collapse of regime

We saw what happened to the Soviet Union after they opened their doors and made reforms!

In other words, realistically, it is yet premature for unification to occur on the Korean peninsula.

That door needs to open before we can move forward.

No Visitors

Although South Korea must continue its engagement policy towards North Korea,

Trust
Aid
Engagement

it is important to not provoke the sensitive North Korean regime.

Come out and play!
Let's negotiate!
Let's host an event together!
I said no! Why do you keep bothering us?

Unification must be pursued on a systematic step-by-step basis.

Skipping a step means drowning!

The South Koreans should look at the reality confronting the Korean peninsula with a cool head.

Reality

Instead of blindly pursuing unification,

Unification

It's dangerous if we go too fast!
Anti-unificationist!

exchanges on economic, academic and artistic levels must first be implemented.

We must start with things that won't shake the very foundation of the regime.

Efforts to study how far the two Koreas have culturally and socially drifted apart should be made

North   South

in order to reduce the gap between the two Koreas,

Vrrm

as, one day, they will indeed become unified!

통일*

* Unification

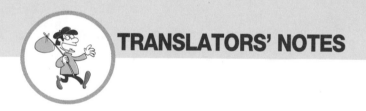

TRANSLATORS' NOTES

Jung Un

As a lawyer specializing in cross-border transactions involving Korea, I am often called upon by my foreign clients to prepare English translations of Korean legal documents, which, of course, are intended to help them understand the Korean legal context of the transactions that they pursue in Korea. In this light, although the translation of *Korea Unmasked*, a comic book, was very different from the translations of legal documents that I usually do, I did find an interesting analogy between the two tasks: Whether it is a particular aspect of the Korean legal system or Korean society that I seek to introduce to the reader, my goal is to always present an accurate picture of Korea and the workings of its society and people, which are often unknown to or, even worse, misunderstood by the outside world.

For all of its faults and shortcomings, which Professor Won-bok Rhie so aptly describes in this book, Korea seduces those who know it. Although highly opinionated, and sometimes prone to generalization, Professor Rhie paradoxically presents an unbiased look at Korean society and its people in an effort to introduce this fascinating and important country to a wider audience. As the editor and co-translator of the English edition of this book, I have attempted to accurately preserve this unbiased picture of Korea that Professor Rhie portrayed in the Korean edition. Any errors in the English edition, of course, are attributable to myself. Through this book, I hope that the reader will come away with a better understanding of Korea and its dynamic society and people.

I am grateful to Ms. Eun-Ju Park of Gimm-Young Publishers, both a client and mentor, for entrusting this project with me.

* * *

Although the Korean convention of referring to the family name first is followed throughout this book (such as in the case of the former Korean presidents), the author and the translators have chosen to indicate their given names first. The reader may note unconventional English spellings of Korean words and names, such as "Joseon" and "Goryeo" (formerly, Choson and Koryo, respectively). This is attributable to recent changes made to the Korean romanization system. The traditional spellings of well-known Korean words such as "chaebol," however, have been preserved due to their widespread usage.

Seoul
September 2002

TRANSLATORS' NOTES

Louis Choi

Professor Won-bok Rhie's comic book is an insightful and innovative look at Asia, Korean history and the Korean people. Like Art Spiegelman's "Maus," the graphic novel format plays a key role in making the story come alive. As a co-translator of this book, my greatest fear was "getting in the way" of such an important piece of work by disrupting the harmony that existed between the Korean words and drawings. Looking at the panel and shot always preceded the translation of a speech balloon or caption (you would be surprised at how many people translate from a text file without ever looking at the illustrations).

The translation of this comic book about Korea aims at accuracy, conveying the intent and message of the author, which, ironically, meant straying from a strictly literal translation of the text. How far do I divagate from a "word for word" translation and what standard of English should be employed? Comic books are different from novels and illustrated books: words and images work together as functional parts of a sentence. After translating Rousseau's "Emile," Allan Bloom wrote that every translation is "in some sense an interpretation; and thus there can be no mechanical rules for translation." My translation of this book is an interpretation, an idea of what I thought the author was trying to convey through the alliance of words and drawings. A literal translation would have eliminated the humor, the inside jokes only a Korean would know, leaving the English reader to sluggishly forge through a dry and awkward representation of Korea. I try to convey the spirit and passion of this book by utilizing the entire English language, vernacular and standard.

My first thanks goes to God for giving me the wisdom and opportunity. I would like to thank the author, Professor Won-bok Rhie, for allowing me to take this fun and educational journey through Korea. I also want to thank Eun-Ju Park of Gimm-Young Publishers for her wonderful advice. She is truly a visionary. I would like to thank Eun-hae Lee, Jean Ryoo, and Sheeny Lee for explaining the Chinese characters mentioned throughout the book. Finally, my mother also helped me greatly, explaining some of the old Korean and Japanese phrases.

New York
September 2002